REVISE PEARSON EDEXCEL GCSE (9–1)

Mathematics

GRADES 7–9
Revision & Practice

Series consultant: Harry Smith
Author: Harry Smith

- -

Also available to support your revision:

Revise GCSE Study Skills Guide   9781292318875

The **Revise GCSE Study Skills Guide** is full of tried-and-trusted hints and tips for how to learn more effectively. It gives you techniques to help you achieve your best — throughout your GCSE studies and beyond.

Revise GCSE Revision Planner   9781292318868

The **Revise GCSE Revision Planner** helps you to plan and organise your time, step-by-step, throughout your GCSE revision. Use this book and wall chart to mastermind your revision.

For the full range of Pearson revision titles across KS2, KS3, GCSE, Functional Skills, AS/A Level and BTEC visit: www.pearsonschools.co.uk/revise

 Pearson

Contents

Use this quick quiz to check that you are confident with the core skills and knowledge you need for the Pearson Edexcel GCSE (9–1) Mathematics Higher exam.

Number

Algebra

Ratio and Proportion

Geometry and Measures

Probability and Statistics

Check your understanding with complete worked solutions to all the Exam practice questions.

A small bit of small print

Pearson Edexcel publishes Sample Assessment Material and the Specification on its website. This is the official content and this book should be used in conjunction with it. The questions in the *Exam practice* sections have been written to help you revise topics and practise answering exam questions. Remember – the real exam questions may not look like this.

Welcome to Nail it!

This book provides revision and practice to help you nail down a top grade in your Pearson Edexcel GCSE (9–1) Mathematics exam. Designed for students aiming for a grade 7, 8 or 9, it's packed with exam tips, support for tricky topics, and exam-style practice questions to make sure you are ready to tackle the toughest questions and achieve top marks.

Track your progress by ticking these boxes.

For more help, check out these pages in the Revise Pearson Edexcel GCSE (9–1) Mathematics Higher Revision Guide.

Revise the key facts for this topic.

Worked exam-style questions show you exactly how to tackle those trickier questions and how to set out your answer.

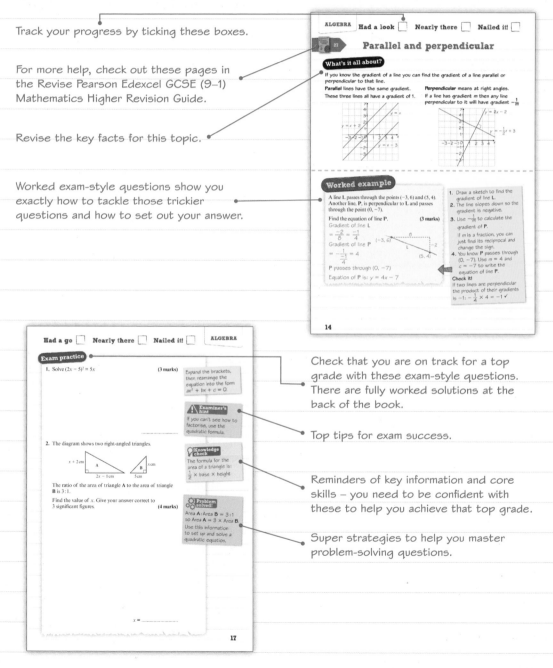

Check that you are on track for a top grade with these exam-style questions. There are fully worked solutions at the back of the book.

Top tips for exam success.

Reminders of key information and core skills – you need to be confident with these to help you achieve that top grade.

Super strategies to help you master problem-solving questions.

💡Knowledge check

If you're aiming for a top grade, you need to be confident with core skills and knowledge, such as solving linear equations or working with fractions, decimals and percentages. Take this quick quiz to find out which skills you might need to brush up on before tackling the topics in this book. Tick the correct answer for each question. The answers are on page 86.

Revise core skills

Use the **Revise Pearson Edexcel GCSE (9–1) Mathematics Revision Guide** if you need to revise any of the core skills covered in this quiz. The green arrow next to each question tells you which page to look at for more help.

1. Express 600 as a product of its prime factors.

- ☐ **A** $2^2 \times 5^2 \times 6$
- ☐ **B** $2^3 \times 3^2 \times 5^3$
- ☐ **C** $2^3 \times 3 \times 5^2$
- ☐ **D** $2 \times 3 \times 10^2$

2. Write $\dfrac{7^{10} \times 7^3}{7}$ as a single power of 7.

- ☐ **A** 7^{29}
- ☐ **B** 7^{12}
- ☐ **C** 7^{23}
- ☐ **D** 7^{-13}

3. Round 0.047 350 8 to 3 significant figures.

- ☐ **A** 0.047
- ☐ **B** 0.0473
- ☐ **C** 0.0474
- ☐ **D** 0.05

4. Work out $1\frac{7}{8} \times 3\frac{2}{5}$

- ☐ **A** $6\frac{3}{8}$
- ☐ **B** $4\frac{9}{13}$
- ☐ **C** $3\frac{7}{20}$
- ☐ **D** $5\frac{1}{8}$

5. Write 736 000 in standard form.

- ☐ **A** 7.36×10^3
- ☐ **B** 736×10^3
- ☐ **C** 7.36×10^5
- ☐ **D** 7.36×10^{-6}

6. The length of a carrot is 20 cm, rounded to the nearest cm. What is the upper bound for this length?

- ☐ **A** 20.5 cm
- ☐ **B** 20.49 cm
- ☐ **C** 25 cm
- ☐ **D** 19.5 cm

7. This combination lock uses two letters from A to Z and two digits from 0 to 9.

Work out the total number of possible combinations.

| C | X | 0 | 5 |

- ☐ **A** 67 600
- ☐ **B** 72
- ☐ **C** 6760
- ☐ **D** 260

8. Simplify $(x^2y)^3$

- ☐ **A** x^2y^3
- ☐ **B** x^5y^3
- ☐ **C** xy^6
- ☐ **D** x^6y^3

9. Expand and simplify $3(4a + b) - 2(a - 2b)$

- ☐ **A** $10a - b$
- ☐ **B** $10a + 7b$
- ☐ **C** $9a + 7b$
- ☐ **D** $5a + b$

10. Expand and simplify $(2x + 3)^2$

- ☐ **A** $4x^2 + 9$
- ☐ **B** $2x^2 + 6x + 9$
- ☐ **C** $4x^2 + 12x + 9$
- ☐ **D** $4x^2 + 6x + 9$

11. Factorise $x^2 - 4x - 12$

- [ ] **A** $4x(x - 3)$
- [ ] **B** $(x - 4)(x + 3)$
- [ ] **C** $(x - 6)(x + 2)$
- [ ] **D** $(x - 4)^2$

12. Solve $6x + 2 = 8x - 1$

- [ ] **A** $x = 0.75$
- [ ] **B** $x = 2$
- [ ] **C** $x = -1$
- [ ] **D** $x = 1.5$

13. $P = 5Q^2 - 2QR$
Find the value of P when $Q = 4$
and $R = -3$

- [ ] **A** 76
- [ ] **B** 104
- [ ] **C** 112
- [ ] **D** 56

14. Find an expression for the nth term
of this sequence.

8   11   14   17   20

- [ ] **A** $3n + 5$
- [ ] **B** $5n + 3$
- [ ] **C** $8n + 3$
- [ ] **D** $20 - 3n$

15. Find the equation of this straight line.

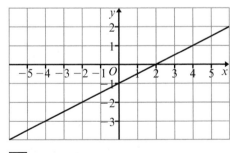

- [ ] **A** $y = 2x - 1$
- [ ] **B** $y = \frac{1}{2}x - 1$
- [ ] **C** $y = -x + 2$
- [ ] **D** $y = 2x + 1$

16. Match this graph to
the correct equation.

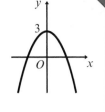

- [ ] **A** $y = 3 - x^2$
- [ ] **B** $y = x^2 - 3$
- [ ] **C** $y = x^2 + 3$
- [ ] **D** $y = x^3$

17. Solve the equation $x^2 - 10x + 16 = 0$

- [ ] **A** $x = 1.6$
- [ ] **B** $x = -4$
- [ ] **C** $x = 8$ or $x = 2$
- [ ] **D** $x = -8$ or $x = -2$

18. Solve the simultaneous equations
$5x + 6y = 5$
$x - 2y = 9$

- [ ] **A** $x = -3, y = 1.5$
- [ ] **B** $x = 4, y = -2.5$
- [ ] **C** $x = 2.5, y = 5$
- [ ] **D** $x = -3, y = -1.5$

19. Solve the inequality $3x + 1 < x - 5$

- [ ] **A** $x > 3$
- [ ] **B** $x > -3$
- [ ] **C** $x < -2$
- [ ] **D** $x < -3$

20. $M = 6R - 20$
Rearrange the formula to make R
the subject.

- [ ] **A** $R = \dfrac{M + 20}{6}$
- [ ] **B** $R = 6M + 20$
- [ ] **C** $R = \dfrac{M}{6} + 20$
- [ ] **D** $R = \dfrac{1}{6}(M - 20)$

21. $f(x) = (2x - 3)^2$
Find $f(-1)$.

☐ **A** −25 ☐ **B** 1

☐ **C** −11 ☐ **D** 25

22. Work out 15% of £900

☐ **A** £145 ☐ **B** £1035

☐ **C** £135 ☐ **D** £180

23. The ratio of juice to water in a
drink is 3:2
The total amount of drink is 600 m*l*.
How much juice is in the drink?

☐ **A** 200 m*l* ☐ **B** 360 m*l*

☐ **C** 400 m*l* ☐ **D** 450 m*l*

24. In a sale, prices are reduced by 20%.
The sale price of a phone is £144.
Work out its original price.

☐ **A** £180 ☐ **B** £172.80

☐ **C** £192 ☐ **D** £115.20

25. A cyclist travels 84 km at an average
speed of 15 km/h.
Work out the total time taken.

☐ **A** 4.5 hours ☐ **B** 0.18 hours

☐ **C** 1260 hours ☐ **D** 5.6 hours

26. The diagram shows a solid
brass cuboid.

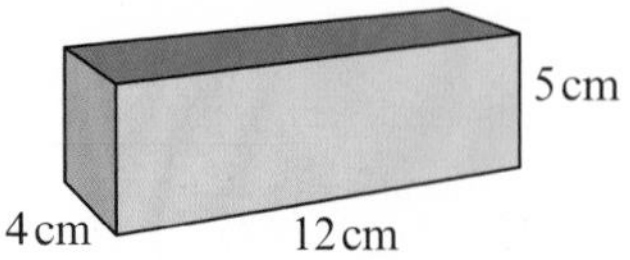

The density of brass is 8.6 g/cm³.
Work out the mass of the cuboid.

☐ **A** 498 g ☐ **B** 27.9 g

☐ **C** 2064 g ☐ **D** 14.3 kg

27. Work out the size of the angle
marked x.

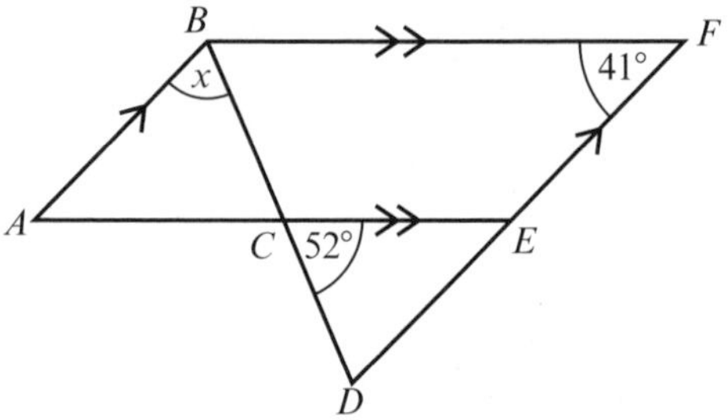

☐ **A** 52° ☐ **B** 9°

☐ **C** 87° ☐ **D** 93°

28. **A** is a regular octagon and **B** is a
regular pentagon.
Work out the size of the angle marked x.

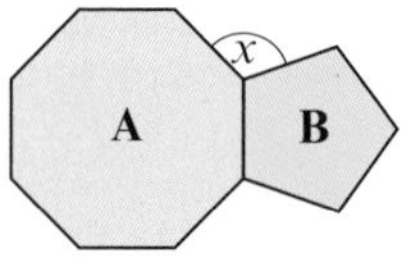

☐ **A** 117° ☐ **B** 135°

☐ **C** 108° ☐ **D** 243°

29. Work out the length of BC in this
right-angled triangle, correct to
1 decimal place.

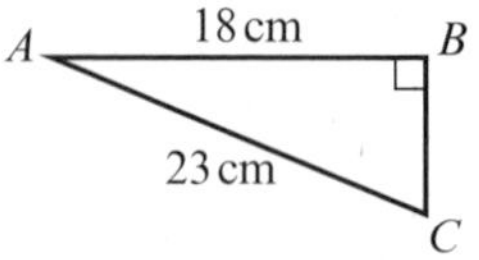

☐ **A** 5.0 cm ☐ **B** 14.3 cm

☐ **C** 29.2 cm ☐ **D** 205.0 cm

30. Work out the size of the
angle marked x in this
right-angled triangle, to
the nearest degree.

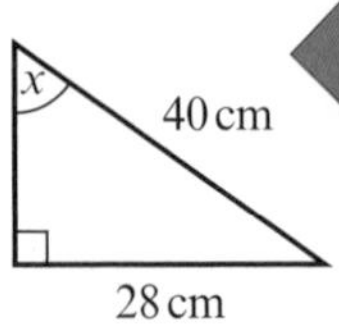

☐ **A** 55° ☐ **B** 35°

☐ **C** 46° ☐ **D** 44°

31. Work out the area of this trapezium.

7.2 m

4.0 m

8.4 m

- [ ] **A** 33.6 m²
- [ ] **B** 62.4 m²
- [ ] **C** 31.2 m²
- [ ] **D** 37.2 m²

32. Work out the volume of this cylinder, to the nearest cm³.

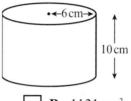

6 cm

10 cm

- [ ] **A** 377 cm³
- [ ] **B** 1131 cm³
- [ ] **C** 360 cm³
- [ ] **D** 1885 cm³

33. Describe fully the single transformation that maps triangle **P** onto triangle **Q**.

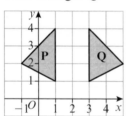

- [ ] **A** Reflection
- [ ] **B** Rotation
- [ ] **C** Rotation 180° about (2, 2.5)
- [ ] **D** Reflection in the line $x = 2$

34. The bearing of point P from point Q is 208°.
Find the bearing of point Q from point P.

- [ ] **A** 018°
- [ ] **B** 28°
- [ ] **C** 028°
- [ ] **D** 388°

106

35. $\mathbf{p} = \begin{pmatrix} -2 \\ 5 \end{pmatrix}$ and $\mathbf{q} = \begin{pmatrix} 3 \\ -3 \end{pmatrix}$

Work out the vector $\mathbf{p} - 2\mathbf{q}$

- [ ] **A** $\begin{pmatrix} 4 \\ -1 \end{pmatrix}$
- [ ] **B** $\begin{pmatrix} -1 \\ 8 \end{pmatrix}$
- [ ] **C** $\begin{pmatrix} -4 \\ 8 \end{pmatrix}$
- [ ] **D** $\begin{pmatrix} -8 \\ 11 \end{pmatrix}$

111

36. The table shows the number of goals scored by a team in 40 matches

Goals	0	1	2	3	4
Frequency	11	15	8	5	1

Work out the mean number of goals scored per match.

- [ ] **A** 2 goals
- [ ] **B** 8 goals
- [ ] **C** 1.25 goals
- [ ] **D** 2.5 goals

123

37. The table shows the probability of each score on a biased dice.

Score	1	2	3	4	5	6
Probability	0.1	x	x	x	x	$2x$

Ravi rolls the dice. Work out the probability that it lands on 6

- [ ] **A** 0.2
- [ ] **B** 0.3
- [ ] **C** 0.36
- [ ] **D** 1.2

123

38. The two-way table shows the number of boys and girls in a class who are left- and right-handed.

	Boys	Girls
Right-handed	11	12
Left-handed	3	4

A girl is picked at random. Work out the probability that she is left-handed.

- [ ] **A** $\frac{1}{4}$
- [ ] **B** $\frac{1}{3}$
- [ ] **C** $\frac{2}{15}$
- [ ] **D** $\frac{7}{30}$

2, 3, 12

Indices and surds

What's it all about?

Learn the index laws for dealing with powers of numbers or letters.

1 $a^m \times a^n = a^{m+n}$

$4^3 \times 4^7 = 4^{3+7} = 4^{10}$

2 $\dfrac{a^m}{a^n} = a^{m-n}$

$12^8 \div 12^3 = 12^{8-3} = 12^5$

3 $(a^m)^n = a^{mn}$

$(7^3)^5 = 7^{3 \times 5} = 7^{15}$

4 $a^{-n} = \dfrac{1}{a^n}$

$5^{-2} = \dfrac{1}{5^2} = \dfrac{1}{25}$

5 $\left(\dfrac{a}{b}\right)^n = \dfrac{a^n}{b^n}$

$\left(\dfrac{3}{10}\right)^2 = \dfrac{3^2}{10^2} = \dfrac{9}{100}$

6 $a^{\frac{1}{n}} = \sqrt[n]{a}$

$81^{\frac{1}{4}} = \sqrt[4]{81} = 3$

Surds

You can use surds to write exact values using square roots.

✓ $\sqrt{ab} = \sqrt{a} \times \sqrt{b}$ $\qquad$ $\sqrt{8} = \sqrt{4} \times \sqrt{2} = 2\sqrt{2}$

✓ $\sqrt{\dfrac{a}{b}} = \dfrac{\sqrt{a}}{\sqrt{b}}$ $\qquad$ $\sqrt{\dfrac{3}{25}} = \dfrac{\sqrt{3}}{\sqrt{25}} = \dfrac{\sqrt{3}}{5}$

Worked example

Show that $(3 - \sqrt{8})^2$ can be written in the form $p + q\sqrt{2}$, where p and q are integers. **(3 marks)**

$(3 - \sqrt{8})(3 - \sqrt{8}) = 9 - 3\sqrt{8} - 3\sqrt{8} + \sqrt{8}\sqrt{8}$

$\qquad\qquad\qquad = 17 - 6\sqrt{8}$

$\qquad\qquad\qquad = 17 - 6 \times 2\sqrt{2}$

$\qquad\qquad\qquad = 17 - 12\sqrt{2}$

💡 Knowledge check

Use **FOIL** to multiply out brackets:

First: 3×3

Outside: $3 \times -\sqrt{8}$

Inside: $-\sqrt{8} \times 3$

Last: $\sqrt{8} \times \sqrt{8} = 8$

Exam practice

1. (a) Work out the value of $\left(\dfrac{27}{64}\right)^{-\frac{2}{3}}$ **(2 marks)**

Work out the powers one step at a time.
Remember $\left(\dfrac{a}{b}\right)^{-1} = \dfrac{b}{a}$

....

(b) $2^x = \dfrac{1}{2}$ $2^y = 4\sqrt{2}$ $2^z = \dfrac{1}{\sqrt{2}}$

Work out the value of $x + y + z$ **(2 marks)**

 Problem solved!

Write each expression as a power of 2 to find the values of x, y and z.

....

2. Show that $\dfrac{20 + \sqrt{12}}{\sqrt{3} + 1}$ can be written in the form $a\sqrt{3} - b$, where a and b are integers.   **(3 marks)**

You need to **rationalise the denominator** in this expression. You can do this by multiplying the top and the bottom of the fraction by $\sqrt{3} - 1$

⚠ **Examiner's hint**

Check that you have written your final answer in the form asked for in the question.

Accuracy and bounds

REVISION GUIDE 10, 11

What's it all about?

When amounts are rounded, the actual amounts could be greater or less than the recorded values. You can show the range of possible actual values using an **error interval**. Here are two examples:

1 If $x = 4.7$ to 1 decimal place, then the error interval for x is
$4.65 \leqslant x < 4.75$

2 If $y = 840$ to 2 significant figures, then the error interval for y is
$835 \leqslant y < 845$

This value is called the **lower bound** for y This value is called the **upper bound** for y

---

To give an answer to an **appropriate degree of accuracy**:

| Calculate the **lower bound** for the answer. | ⟹ | Calculate the **upper bound** for the answer. | ⟹ | Choose the most accurate value that **both bounds** would round to. |

Worked example

A cylinder has a volume of 115 cm^3, to the nearest cm^3. Its radius is 2.3 cm, correct to 1 decimal place.

Find the height of the cylinder to an appropriate degree of accuracy. You must explain why your answer is to this degree of accuracy. **(4 marks)**

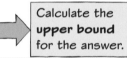

	Upper bound	Lower bound
Volume	115.5 cm^3	114.5 cm^3
Radius	2.35 cm	2.25 cm

UB for height $= \dfrac{115.5}{\pi \times 2.25^2} = 7.26218\ldots$

LB for height $= \dfrac{114.5}{\pi \times 2.35^2} = 6.59963\ldots$

Height $= 7 \text{ cm}$ (1 s.f.)

UB and LB both round to 7 cm to 1 s.f.

Problem solved!

height $= \dfrac{\text{volume}}{\pi \times \text{radius}^2}$

To find the **upper** bound for the height, use the upper bound for the volume and the lower bound for the radius.

To find the **lower** bound for the height, use the lower bound for the volume and the upper bound for the height.

Exam practice

1.

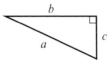

$a = 20\,$m to the nearest metre.
$b = 17\,$m to the nearest metre.

Calculate the lower bound for c. **(4 marks)**

⚠ **Examiner's hint**

If you are using bounds in a question, it's a good idea to write the upper and lower bounds for each value before you start.

💡 **Knowledge check**

Use Pythagoras' theorem: $a^2 = b^2 + c^2$

.... m

2. Poppy is riding her bike to school. She travels a distance of $0.85\,$km, at an average speed of $7.1\,$m/s.
Both figures are correct to 2 significant figures.

By considering bounds, work out the time taken for Poppy to complete her journey. Give your answer to a suitable degree of accuracy.

You must show your working and give a reason for your final answer. **(5 marks)**

💡 **Knowledge check**

Learn the formula triangle for speed, distance and time:

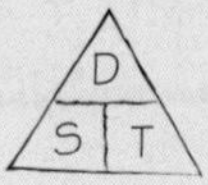

$$\frac{D}{S \mid T}$$

Make sure your units are consistent before using the formula.

You need to work out the upper and lower bounds for the time, then choose the most accurate value that **both** of these bounds would round to.

17, 18

Brackets and factorising

What's it all about?

Expanding triple brackets

Follow these two steps to expand the product of **three factors**:

 Choose two of the factors. Expand and simplify them, then write brackets around the result.

 Multiply every term in this expression by **each** term in the third factor. Then simplify by collecting like terms.

Factorising $ax^2 + bx + c$

If the coefficient of x^2 is more than 1, find two numbers that add up to b and multiply to make ac. For example:

$8x^2 + 22x + 15$

$ac = 120 = 12 \times 10$, and $12 + 10 = 22$

so $8x^2 + 22x + 15$

$= 8x^2 + 10x + 12x + 15$

$= 2x(4x + 5) + 3(4x + 5)$

$= (4x + 5)(2x + 3)$

Difference of two squares

You can factorise expressions that are written as

$(\text{something})^2 - (\text{something else})^2$

Use this rule:

$a^2 - b^2 = (a + b)(a - b)$

$x^2 - 36 = x^2 - (6)^2$

$= (x + 6)(x - 6)$

36 is a square number.

$36 = 6^2$ so $a = x$ and $b = 6$

Worked example

Show that

$(x + 5)^2(3x - 2) = 3x^3 + 28x^2 + 55x - 50$

for all values of x.   **(3 marks)**

$(x + 5)(x + 5)(3x - 2) = (x^2 + 10x + 25)(3x - 2)$

$= 3x^3 + 30x^2 + 75x - 2x^2 - 20x - 50$

$= 3x^3 + 28x^2 + 55x - 50$

Knowledge check

$(x + 5)^2 = (x + 5)(x + 5)$

$= x^2 + 10x + 25$

Examiner's hint

In a 'show that' question you must show each step of your working clearly.

Exam practice

1. Factorise $5x^2 + 13x + 6$ **(2 marks)**

> $ac = 30$ and $b = 13$, so look for two numbers that add up to 13 and multiply to make 30. Use these numbers to split the x term into two terms.

....

2. Show that $(2x + 1)(x - 5)(4x - 3)$ can be written in the form $ax^3 + bx^2 + cx + d$ where a, b, c and d are positive integers.   **(3 marks)**

> **Problem solved!**
>
> Use the x^3 term and the number term to check your answer:
>
> $2x \times x \times 4x = 8x^3$
> so $a = 8$
>
> $1 \times -5 \times -3 = 15$
> so $d = 15$

3. (a) Factorise $x^2 - y^2$ **(2 marks)**

....

   (b) Hence, or otherwise, simplify fully
   $(p^2 + q^2)^2 - (p^2 - q^2)^2$ **(3 marks)**

> **Examiner's hint**
>
> If a question says 'Hence, or otherwise' you can save time by using your earlier answer. In this case, set $x = p^2 + q^2$ and $y = p^2 - q^2$ and use the answer to part (a).

....

25, 26

Straight-line graphs

What's it all about?

You need to be able to find the equations of straight lines confidently.

1   Given one point and the gradient:

> Substitute the gradient for m in $y = mx + c$

⬇

> Substitute the x- and y-values given into the equation

⬇

> Solve the equation to find c

⬇

> Write out the equation

2   Given two points:

> Draw a sketch showing the two points

⬇

> Work out the gradient of the line using a triangle

⬇

> Use method 1 (on the left) and one of the points given to find the equation

---

Mid-points

A **line segment** is a short section of a straight line.

You can find the **mid-point** of a line segment if you know the coordinates of the ends.

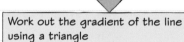

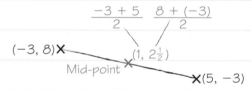

$(-3, 8)$✕

Mid-point

$(1, 2\frac{1}{2})$✕

✕$(5, -3)$

Coordinates of mid-point = (average of x-coordinates, average of y-coordinates)

Worked example

A line passes through the points with coordinates (1, 5) and (2, 7).

Find the equation of the line.   **(3 marks)**

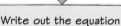

(2,7)

(1,5)   2

1

Gradient, $m = \dfrac{2}{1} = 2$

Equation of line: $y = mx + c \rightarrow y = 2x + c$

For point (1, 5), $x = 1$, $y = 5$

Substitute these values into the equation:

$5 = 2 + c \rightarrow c = 3$

The equation is $y = 2x + 3$

> ⚠ **Examiner's hint**
>
> Drawing a sketch will help you check that your answer makes sense.

> 💡 **Knowledge check**
>
> The equation of a straight line is $y = mx + c$, where m is the gradient and (0, c) is the y-intercept.

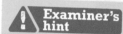
Exam practice

1. The line **L** has gradient 3 and passes through the point (2, 1).

   Find the equation of the line.   **(2 marks)**

2. A straight line passes through the points (2, 7) and (8, −1).

   Find the equation of the line. Give your answer in the form $ax + by = c$, where a, b and c are integers.   **(3 marks)**

3. A straight line passes through the points with coordinates $(-5, 2)$, $(1, k)$ and $(3, 2k)$.

   Find the equation of the line.   **(4 marks)**

27

Parallel and perpendicular

What's it all about?

If you know the gradient of a line you can find the gradient of a line parallel or perpendicular to that line.

Parallel lines have the same gradient.

These three lines all have a gradient of 1.

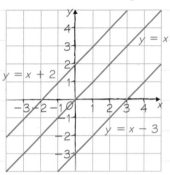

Perpendicular means at right angles.

If a line has gradient m then any line perpendicular to it will have gradient $-\frac{1}{m}$

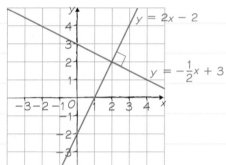

Worked example

A line **L** passes through the points $(-3, 6)$ and $(5, 4)$. Another line, **P**, is perpendicular to **L** and passes through the point $(0, -7)$.

Find the equation of line **P**. **(3 marks)**

Gradient of line **L**

$= \frac{-2}{8} = \frac{-1}{4}$

Gradient of line **P**

$= -\frac{1}{\frac{-1}{4}} = 4$

P passes through $(0, -7)$

Equation of **P** is: $y = 4x - 7$

1. Draw a sketch to find the gradient of line **L**.

2. The line slopes down so the gradient is negative.

3. Use $-\frac{1}{m}$ to calculate the gradient of **P**.

   If m is a fraction, you can just find its reciprocal and change the sign.

4. You know **P** passes through $(0, -7)$. Use $m = 4$ and $c = -7$ to write the equation of line **P**.

Check it!

If two lines are perpendicular the product of their gradients is -1: $-\frac{1}{4} \times 4 = -1$ ✓

14

Exam practice

1. The diagram shows a parallelogram.

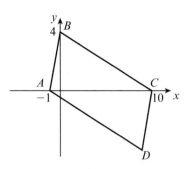

Find the equation of the line that passes through C and is perpendicular to AD. **(4 marks)**

....

Knowledge check

A parallelogram has two pairs of parallel sides, so CD is parallel to AB.

Sketch the line on the diagram, and check that the equation looks roughly correct.

2. The point A has coordinates $(p, 2p)$
The point B has coordinates $(7, 4)$
The line with equation $5y - 2x = 3$ is parallel to the line segment AB.

Find the value of p. **(4 marks)**

$p =$ ....

Problem solved!

Start by writing an expression for the gradient of AB in terms of p.

Knowledge check

To find the gradient of the line with equation $5y - 2x = 3$, rearrange it into the form $y = mx + c$.

31, 32

Quadratic equations

What's it all about?

Quadratic equations can have two real solutions, one real solution or no real solutions. To solve a quadratic equation, write it in the form:

$$ax^2 + bx + c = 0$$

1 If you can, **factorise** the left-hand side then set each factor equal to zero and solve to find the solutions.

2 You can use the **quadratic formula**:

$$x = \frac{-b \pm \sqrt{b^2 - 4ac}}{2a}$$

Worked example

The diagram shows a rectangle. The measurements are given in cm.

$x + 4$

$2x + 1$

The area of the rectangle is 60 cm.

Find the perimeter of the rectangle. **(5 marks)**

$(2x + 1)(x + 4) = 60$

$2x^2 + 8x + x + 4 = 60$

$2x^2 + 9x - 56 = 0$

Method 1

$(2x - 7)(x + 8) = 0$

$2x - 7 = 0$ or $x + 8 = 0$

$x = \frac{7}{2}$ $\qquad x = -8$

Method 2

$x = \frac{-9 \pm \sqrt{9^2 - 4 \times 2 \times (-56)}}{2 \times 2}$

$= \frac{-9 \pm 23}{4}$

$= 3.5$ or -8

length = 8, width = 7.5, so

perimeter = $2 \times 8 + 2 \times 7.5 = 31$ cm

You might need to form and solve a quadratic equation to solve a problem
Set the area of the rectangle equal to 60, then rearrange and solve the equation

Problem solved!

Lengths must be positive numbers. If $x = -8$ then both dimensions would be negative, so you can ignore this solution.

Exam practice

1. Solve $(2x - 5)^2 = 5x$ **(3 marks)**

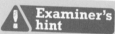

Expand the brackets, then rearrange the equation into the form $ax^2 + bx + c = 0$.

⚠ **Examiner's hint**

If you can't see how to factorise, use the quadratic formula.

....

2. The diagram shows two right-angled triangles.

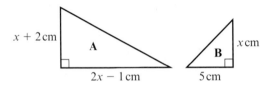

$x + 2\,$cm   **A** $2x - 1\,$cm   **B** $x\,$cm $5\,$cm

💡 **Knowledge check**

The formula for the area of a triangle is:

$\frac{1}{2}$ × base × height

The ratio of the area of triangle **A** to the area of triangle **B** is $3 : 1$.

Find the value of x. Give your answer correct to 3 significant figures.   **(4 marks)**

 Problem solved!

Area **A** : Area **B** = 3 : 1 so Area **A** = 3 × Area **B**.

Use this information to set up and solve a quadratic equation.

$x = $ ....

REVISION GUIDE 22–24

Sequences

What's it all about?

In an **arithmetic** sequence the **difference** between consecutive terms is constant.

−2.5   −2.5   −2.5   −2.5

4   1.5   −1   −3.5   −6

In a **geometric** sequence the **ratio** between consecutive terms is constant.

×3   ×3   ×3   ×3

3   9   27   81   243 ...

Quadratic sequences

The nth term of a quadratic sequence can be written as

$$u_n = an^2 + bn + c$$

where a, b and c are numbers and $a \neq 0$.

Finding nth terms

You can find the nth term of a quadratic sequence by looking at the **second differences**. The sequence with nth term $an^2 + bn + c$ will have second differences equal to $2a$.

Worked example

The first five terms of a quadratic sequence are

3   11   25   45   71

Find an expression, in terms of n, for the nth term of this sequence.   **(3 marks)**

3   11   25   45   71

   +8   +14   +20   +26

      +6   +6   +6

The second difference is +6, so the coefficient of n^2 will be 3.

$2a = 6$ so $a = 3$

$u_n = 3n^2 + bn + c$

n	1	2	3	4	5
u_n	3	11	25	45	71
$3n^2$	3	12	27	48	75
$u_n - 3n^2$	0	−1	−2	−3	−4

Work out $u_n - 3n^2$ for each term. This will be an arithmetic sequence.

$u_n - 3n^2 = -n + 1$

So $u_n = 3n^2 - n + 1$

Exam practice

1. The first three terms of a geometric sequence are
$$8 \quad 2p \quad p + 12$$
where p is a positive constant.

(a) Find the value of p. **(3 marks)**

Problem solved!

The sequence is geometric so the ratios between consecutive terms are constant:
$$\frac{2p}{8} = \frac{p + 12}{2p}$$

$p =$ ....

(b) Find the 5th term of the sequence. **(2 marks)**

....

2. Here are the first five terms of a sequence.
$$3 \quad 10 \quad 21 \quad 36 \quad 55$$
Find an expression, in terms of n, for the nth term of this sequence. **(3 marks)**

This is a quadratic sequence. Find the second differences then draw a table like the one in the Worked example opposite.

....

3. The rule to get from one term to the next term in a sequence is:

| Add 3 then multiply by k |

where k is a positive constant. The second term is 19 and the fourth term is 145.

Find the first term in the sequence. **(5 marks)**

Use the second term to find an expression for the fourth term in terms of k.

Examiner's hint

Don't assume that answers will be integers.

....

33, 43

Completing the square

What's it all about?

You can use **completed square form** $(x + p)^2 + q$ or $a(x + p)^2 + q$ to solve quadratic equations and find the turning points of graphs. Use this identity to help you complete the square when the coefficient of x^2 is 1:

$$x^2 + bx + c \equiv \left(x + \frac{b}{2}\right)^2 - \left(\frac{b}{2}\right)^2 + c$$

Halve the x-coefficient to find the number in the brackets. Then subtract the square of this number outside the brackets.

$-\left(\frac{b}{2}\right)^2 + c$ are number terms so you can combine them.

Turning points

The graph of $y = (x - a)^2 + b$ has a turning point at (a, b). You can think of it as a translation of the graph of $y = x^2$ by the vector $\binom{a}{b}$.

There is more about transformations of graphs on page 28.

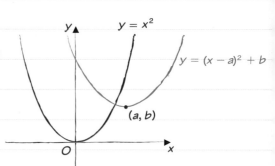

Worked example

(a) Show that $3x^2 + 24x - 1$ can be written in the form $a(x + p)^2 + q$ where a, p and q are integers.
(3 marks)

$3x^2 + 24x - 1 = 3(x^2 + 8x) - 1$
$\qquad = 3((x + 4)^2 - 16) - 1$
$\qquad = 3(x + 4)^2 - 48 - 1$
$\qquad = 3(x + 4)^2 - 49$

(b) Hence write down the coordinates of the turning point on the graph with equation $y = 3x^2 + 24x - 1$.
(1 mark)

$(-4, -49)$

⚙️ **Problem solved!**

You can complete the square in $ax^2 + bx + c$ when $a \neq 1$ by taking a factor of a out of the first two terms.

$x^2 + 8x = (x + 4)^2 - 4^2$

The turning point will occur when $(x + 4)^2 = 0$. This happens when $x = -4$.

Exam practice

1. (a) Write $x^2 + 10x - 7$ in the form $(x + a)^2 - b$, where a and b are integers to be found. **(2 marks)**

> You can solve a quadratic equation by completing the square and using inverse operations:
> $$(x + a)^2 - b = 0$$
> $$(x + a)^2 = b$$
> $$x + a = \pm\sqrt{b}$$
> $$x = -a \pm \sqrt{b}$$

(b) Hence, or otherwise, solve the equation $x^2 + 10x = 7$, giving your answer in the form $x = p \pm q\sqrt{2}$, where p and q are integers. **(2 marks)**

....

2. $f(x) = x^2 - 6x + 15$

(a) Sketch the graph of $y = f(x)$. Show clearly the coordinates of the turning point, and the coordinates of any points where the curve crosses the coordinate axes. **(5 marks)**

Knowledge check

A quadratic graph with a positive x^2 coefficient is a U shape. Substitute $x = 0$ to find the value of y when the curve crosses the y-axis.

> ⚠ **Examiner's hint**
>
> Use a sharp pencil, and a ruler to draw your axes. Label points clearly and draw a smooth curve.

(b) State, with a reason, the number of real solutions to the equation $f(x) = 0$. **(2 marks)**

....

....

Knowledge check

The solutions to $f(x) = 0$ will be the x-coordinates at the points where the curve $y = f(x)$ crosses the x-axis.

Simultaneous equations

What's it all about?

Simultaneous equations have two unknowns. You need to find a pair (or pairs) of values that make **both** equations true at the same time. Follow these steps to solve one linear and one quadratic simultaneous equation:

| Rearrange the linear equation into the form $x = ...$ or $y = ...$ | → | Substitute into the quadratic equation and solve the resulting quadratic equation. | → | Substitute each answer back into the linear equation to find the value of the other variable. |

Intersections of graphs

Solutions to simultaneous equations can represent points of intersection of graphs. When one equation is linear and one is quadratic there can be no points of intersection, one point, or two points.

Two solutions

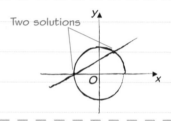

Worked example

Solve the simultaneous equations

$x - 2y = 1$ ①

$x^2 + y^2 = 13$ ②   **(5 marks)**

$x = 1 + 2y$ ③

Substitute ③ into ②:

$(1 + 2y)^2 + y^2 = 13$

$1 + 4y + 4y^2 + y^2 = 13$

$5y^2 + 4y - 12 = 0$

$(5y - 6)(y + 2) = 0$

$y = \dfrac{6}{5}$ or $y = -2$

$x = 1 + 2\left(\dfrac{6}{5}\right)$ $x = 1 + 2(-2)$

$= \dfrac{17}{5}$ $= -3$

Solutions: $x = \dfrac{17}{5}, y = \dfrac{6}{5}$ and

$x = -3, y = -2$

This equation has **two pairs** of solutions. Each solution is an x-value **and** a y-value. You need to find four values in total, and pair them up correctly.

You can substitute for x or y. It is easier to substitute for x because there will be no fractions.
Use brackets to make sure that the whole expression is squared.
Rearrange the quadratic equation for y into the form $ay^2 + by + c = 0$
Factorise the left-hand side to find two solutions for y.
Substitute each value of y into one of the original equations to find the corresponding values of x.

Exam practice

1. A circle has equation $x^2 + y^2 = 10$
   A straight line has equation $y + 2x = 7$

   Find the coordinates of the points where the circle and the line intersect. **(6 marks)**

   > Look for ways to make your working easier. The coefficient of y in the second equation is 1, so it will be easier to rearrange for y and then substitute.

2. The diagram shows the curve with equation $y = x^2 - 3x + 4$ and the straight line with equation $y = 3x - 5$

   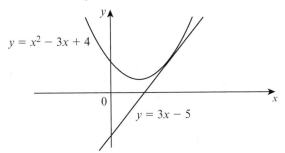

   Prove algebraically that the line is a tangent to the curve. **(5 marks)**

    Knowledge check

   A **tangent** touches the curve at one point only.

   Problem solved!

   Solve the two equations simultaneously:

   - **No solutions** means the curve and line don't intersect.
   - **One solution** means they intersect at one point (so the line is a tangent).
   - **Two solutions** mean they intersect at two points.

36

Equation of a circle

What's it all about?

A circle of radius r with its centre at the origin has equation

$$x^2 + y^2 = r^2 \bullet \longrightarrow \text{The radius is } \textbf{squared}$$

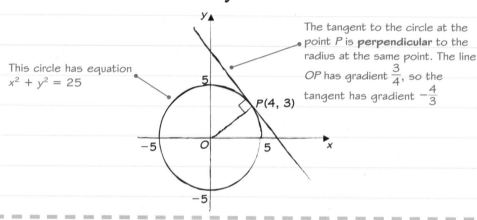

This circle has equation
$x^2 + y^2 = 25$

The tangent to the circle at the point P is **perpendicular** to the radius at the same point. The line OP has gradient $\frac{3}{4}$, so the tangent has gradient $-\frac{4}{3}$

$P(4, 3)$

Worked example

The circle **C** has equation $x^2 + y^2 = 100$
The line **L** is a tangent to the circle at the point $(6, -8)$
Find the equation of **L**.   **(5 marks)**

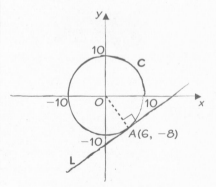

Gradient of $OA = -\dfrac{8}{6} = -\dfrac{4}{3}$

So gradient of $L = \dfrac{3}{4}$

Equation of L is $y = \dfrac{3}{4}x + c$

L passes through $(6, -8)$ so

$-8 = \dfrac{3}{4} \times 6 + c$

$c = -12.5$

So the equation of L is $y = \dfrac{3}{4}x - 12.5$

⚠ Examiner's hint

Draw a large clearly labelled sketch showing the tangent and the radius at the point $(6, -8)$.

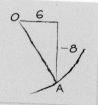

Exam practice

1. The equation of circle **C** is $x^2 + y^2 = 36$

The circle **C** is translated by vector $\begin{pmatrix} 0 \\ 2 \end{pmatrix}$ to give circle **B**.

Draw a sketch of circle **B**, labelling the centre of the circle and any points of intersection with the y-axis.   **(3 marks)**

Knowledge check

The top number in a translation vector tells you the distance to the **right** and the bottom number tells you the distance **up**.

Examiner's hint

Use a pair of compasses to draw your circle neatly.

2. A circle has equation $x^2 + y^2 = k$

The point P with coordinates $(8, 2)$ lies on the circle.

(a)   Find the value of k.   **(1 mark)**

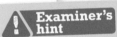

Substitute $x = 8$ and $y = 2$ into the equation to find the value of k

$$k = \text{..........................}$$

The line **L** is a tangent to the circle at P. The line **L** crosses the y-axis at the point Q.

(b)   Find the area of triangle OPQ.   **(5 marks)**

Examiner's hint

Read the question carefully.

The three vertices of the triangle are the origin, the point $(8, 2)$ and the y-intercept of the tangent.

Knowledge check

Use $\frac{1}{2}$ × base × height to find the area of the triangle.

$$\text{..........................} \text{ units}^2$$

38

Quadratic inequalities

What's it all about?

You can solve a quadratic inequality by considering **critical values**.

| Replace the inequality with an = sign. | → | Solve to find the critical values. | → | Use substitution or a sketch to choose the correct set of values. |

Worked example

n is an integer such that $3n - 5 \leqslant 1$ and $2n^2 - 5n < 3$

Find all the possible values of n. **(5 marks)**

$3n - 5 \leqslant 1$

$\qquad 3n \leqslant 6$

$\qquad n \leqslant 2$

$\qquad 2n^2 - 5n = 3$

$2n^2 - 5n - 3 = 0$

$(2n + 1)(n - 3) = 0$

Critical values are $-\dfrac{1}{2}$ and 3

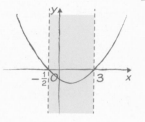

Possible values are 0, 1, 2.

Knowledge check

You can use inverse operations to solve a **linear** inequality. If you multiply or divide by a negative number you need to reverse the direction of the inequality.

For the quadratic inequality, replace < with = and solve to find the critical values. Use a sketch to determine which set of values satisfies the inequality.

⚠ Examiner's hint

Use a number line to choose the integers that satisfy **both** inequalities.

Exam practice

1. The diagram shows a proposed layout for a building plot. The measurements are in metres. The area allocated to the house is a square.

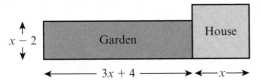

According to planning regulations, the area for the garden must be at least twice the area for the house.

Find the range of possible values of x. Show all of your working. **(5 marks)**

Problem solved!
Read the question carefully, then translate the word problem into an algebra problem.

Remember that lengths cannot be negative numbers.

....

2. Solve $7 < \dfrac{x^2 + 7}{8} < 11$ **(5 marks)**

Problem solved!
This is two separate inequalities:

$7 < \dfrac{x^2 + 7}{8}$

and

$\dfrac{x^2 + 7}{8} < 11$

The safest approach is to solve them separately then identify the values that satisfy **both**.

....

40

Transforming graphs

What's it all about?

You can use functions to describe a **translation** or a **reflection** of a graph.
If you start with the graph $y = f(x)$:

 $y = f(x + a)$ is a translation by the vector $\begin{pmatrix} -a \\ 0 \end{pmatrix}$

 $y = f(x) + a$ is a translation by the vector $\begin{pmatrix} 0 \\ a \end{pmatrix}$

 $y = -f(x)$ is a reflection in the x-axis

 $y = f(-x)$ is a reflection in the y-axis

Trigonometric graphs

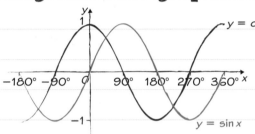

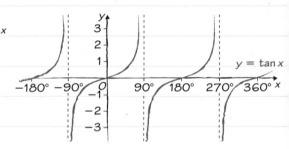

The graph of $y = \sin x$ is a translation of $y = \cos x$ by 90° to the right.

You also need to know the shape of the graph of $y = \tan x$.

Worked example

The grid shows the graph with equation $y = f(x)$.
On the same grid, draw a sketch of the graph
with equation $y = f(-x) + 1$　　　　**(2 marks)**

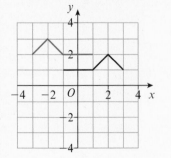

 Problem solved!

There are **two transformations** to carry out. Do them one at a time: a reflection in the y-axis followed by a translation by vector $\begin{pmatrix} 0 \\ 1 \end{pmatrix}$

 The answer is shown in red.

28

Exam practice

1. The graph of $y = f(x)$ is drawn on both grids.

   (a) On this grid draw the graph of $y = -f(x)$ **(1 mark)**

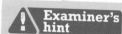
Examiner's hint

Use a ruler and a sharp pencil whenever you have to draw straight lines on graphs.

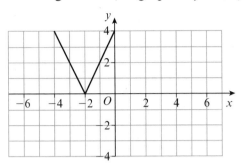

   (b) On this grid draw the graph of $y = f(x + 2)$ **(1 mark)**

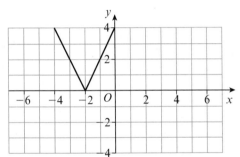

Watch out! For the transformation $y = f(x + a)$, if a is positive the graph moves to the left.

2. The graph of $y = f(x)$ is tranformed to give the graph of $y = -f(x - 4)$

   The point P on the graph of $y = f(x)$ is transformed to the point Q on the graph of $y = -f(x - 4)$
   P has coordinates (3, 1).

   Write down the coordinates of Q.   **(2 marks)**

Draw your own sketch, and carry out the two transformations one at a time.

(............., ...)

45

Iteration

What's it all about?

You can use an **iteration formula** to find solutions to some equations. In your exam you will be told if you need to use an iteration formula.

Solutions

If f(x) **changes sign** between two values of x, then you know that f(x) = 0 has a solution between these two values.

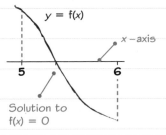

$y = f(x)$

x-axis

5

6

Solution to f(x) = 0

Using a calculator

You can find iteration values quickly on a calculator. Work out the first value, then replace x_n with the (Ans) function and keep pressing (=).

$-5+\dfrac{2}{\text{Ans}^2}$

-4.916743333

Worked example

Use the iteration formula $x_{n+1} = -5 + \dfrac{2}{x_n^2}$ with

$x_0 = -2$ to find the values of x_1, x_2 and x_3. **(3 marks)**

$x_1 = -5 + \dfrac{2}{x_0^2} = -5 + \dfrac{2}{(-2)^2}$

$\quad = -4.5$

$x_2 = -5 + \dfrac{2}{x_1^2} = -5 + \dfrac{2}{(-4.5)^2}$

$\quad = -4.901234568$

$x_3 = -5 + \dfrac{2}{x_2^2} = -5 + \dfrac{2}{(-4.901...)^2}$

$\quad = -4.916743333$

If you replace x_{n+1} and x_n with x, you can rearrange the iteration formula to get $x^3 + 5x^2 = 2$. The values x_1, x_2, x_3... get closer and closer to the solution to this equation.

Exam practice

(a) Show that $6x - x^3 - 3 = 0$ has a solution between
$x = 0$ and $x = 1$ **(2 marks)**

Work out the value of
$6x - x^3 - 3$ at
$x = 0$ and at $x = 1$,
then write a
short conclusion.

(b) Show that the equation $6x - x^3 - 3 = 0$ can be rearranged
to give $x = \dfrac{3}{6 - x^2}$ **(2 marks)**

Knowledge check
To rearrange an
equation you need to
apply the same
operation to each side.

(c) Starting with $x_0 = 1$, use the iteration formula
$x_{n+1} = \dfrac{3}{6 - x_n{}^2}$ to estimate a solution to $6x - x^3 - 3 = 0$.
Give your answer to 2 decimal places. **(3 marks)**

Problem solved!
You are not told how
many times to apply
the formula. Keep going
until you find two values
that round to the same
amount to 2 d.p.

....

(d) Explain how you know that your answer in part (c) is
correct to 2 decimal places. **(2 marks)**

Problem solved!
Work out the value of
$6x - x^3 - 3$ at points
0.005 above and
below your value.

....

....

47, 48

Algebraic fractions

What's it all about?

You can simplify algebraic fractions by dividing the top and bottom by a common factor.

The **golden rule** is to factorise expressions as much as possible before cancelling.

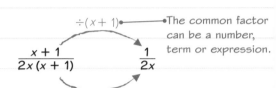

$\div(x+1)$ •—— •The common factor can be a number, term or expression.

$$\frac{x+1}{2x(x+1)} \qquad \frac{1}{2x}$$

$\div(x+1)$

---

 1 To **add or subtract**, find equivalent fractions with the same denominator, then add or subtract the numerators.

 2 To **multiply**, multiply the numerators and multiply the denominators.

 3 To **divide**, turn the second fraction upside down and then multiply.

Quadratic equations

You can use these techniques to solve harder quadratic equations:

$$\frac{x}{2x-3} + \frac{4}{x+1} = 1$$

Multiply by the common denominator:

$(2x-3)(x+1)$

$$\frac{x(x+1)}{(2x-3)(x+1)} + \frac{4(2x-3)}{(2x-3)(x+1)} = 1$$

$$x(x+1) + 4(2x-3) = (2x-3)(x+1)$$

$$x^2 + x + 8x - 12 = 2x^2 - 3x + 2x - 3$$

$$x^2 - 10x + 9 = 0$$

You can solve this by factorising.

Worked example

Simplify $\dfrac{3x^2 - 8x - 3}{x^2 - 9}$ **(3 marks)**

$$\frac{3x^2 - 8x - 3}{x^2 - 9} = \frac{(3x+1)(x-3)}{(x+3)(x-3)}$$

$$= \frac{3x+1}{x+3}$$

You need to factorise the top and the bottom of the fraction before you can simplify. Remember that $a^2 - b^2 = (a+b)(a-b)$

Exam practice

1. Write $\dfrac{9x^2 - 1}{3x^2 - 8x - 3}$ in the form $\dfrac{ax + b}{cx + d}$, where a, b, c and d are integers.   **(3 marks)**

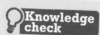

Factorise the top and bottom of the fraction.

....

Knowledge check

Integers can include negative numbers or zero.

2. (a) Express $\dfrac{6}{x} - \dfrac{2}{x + 2}$ as a single fraction in its simplest form.   **(2 marks)**

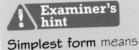

Examiner's hint

Simplest form means that you have collected like terms and cancelled where possible. You can leave numerators and denominators factorised, or you can expand the brackets.

....

(b) Hence, or otherwise, solve

$$\dfrac{6}{x} - \dfrac{2}{x + 2} + \dfrac{1}{2} = 0$$ **(3 marks)**

....

3. Show that $\dfrac{3x}{x^2 - 5x} \div \dfrac{12x + 6}{2x^2 - 9x - 5} = \dfrac{1}{2}$ **(3 marks)**

Knowledge check

To divide by a fraction you turn it upside down then multiply.
This rule works for algebraic fractions as well.

50, 51

Functions

What's it all about?

A function is like a number machine – it has an input and an output.

If you apply one function after another you get a **composite function**.

The function that reverses another function is called its **inverse**.

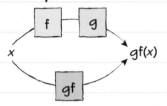

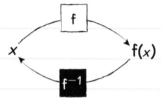

Finding the inverse

To find the inverse of a function given in the form f(x) = ... you need to:

| Write the function in the form $y = ...$ | Rearrange to make x the subject. | Swap any y's for x's and rewrite as $f^{-1}(x) = ...$ |

Worked example

The function f is defined as

$$f(x) = \frac{3x}{x-1}$$

Find an expression for $f^{-1}(x)$ **(3 marks)**

$$y = \frac{3x}{x-1}$$

$$xy - y = 3x$$

$$xy - 3x = y$$

$$x(y-3) = y$$

$$x = \frac{y}{y-3}$$

$$f^{-1}(x) = \frac{x}{x-3}$$

💡 **Knowledge check**

The x-term appears twice here. When you rearrange you need to collect the x-terms together then factorise to get x on its own.

⚠️ **Examiner's hint**

Make sure you write your final answer as an expression in terms of x, not y.

Exam practice

1. The functions f and g are such that

$$f(x) = 1 - x^2 \text{ and } g(x) = 3x - 1$$

   (a) Show that $fg(x) = 3x(2 - 3x)$ **(3 marks)**

   fg(x) means you do
   g(x) first. Use the
   whole expression
   for g(x) as the input
   for f(x). Then simplify
   and factorise.

   (b) Find $g^{-1}(0)$ **(2 marks)**

   ....

2. The functions f and g are defined as

$$f(x) = px + q$$
$$g(x) = 3x + 2$$

   where p and q are constants.

   Given that $f(2) = 7$ and $f(3) = g^{-1}(35)$, find the
   value of p and the value of q.   **(5 marks)**

   Problem solved!
   Use the information
   given in the question
   to write two
   simultaneous equations
   involving p and q.

   You can find the value
   of $g^{-1}(35)$ by working
   'backwards' through
   the function: subtract
   2 then divide by 3.

   $p =$ ....

   $q =$ ....

Algebraic proof

What's it all about?

To **prove** an algebraic statement you need to show that it is true for any numbers. You can use the rules shown on the right for odd and even integers in some algebraic proofs.

	Product	Sum
odd and odd	odd	even
odd and even	even	odd
even and even	even	even

Algebraic proof toolkit

Use n to represent any whole number.

Number fact	Written using algebra
even number	$2n$
odd number	$2n + 1$ or $2n - 1$
multiple of 3	$3n$
consecutive numbers	$n, n + 1, n + 2, \ldots$
consecutive even numbers	$2n, 2n + 2, 2n + 4, \ldots$
consecutive odd numbers	$2n + 1, 2n + 3, 2n + 5, \ldots$
consecutive square numbers	$n^2, (n + 1)^2, (n + 2)^2, \ldots$

Worked example

Prove that the sum of three consecutive integers is always divisible by 3. **(3 marks)**

n, $n + 1$ and $n + 2$ represent any three consecutive integers.

$$n + (n + 1) + (n + 2) = 3n + 3$$
$$= 3(n + 1)$$

$n + 1$ is an integer, so $3(n + 1)$ is divisible by 3.

Problem solved!

To **prove** the statement you need to show that it is true for **any** three consecutive integers. You can do this using algebra.

1. Write the first integer as n and the next two integers as $n + 1$ and $n + 2$.

2. Write an expression for the sum of your three integers.

3. Simplify and factorise the expression.

4. Explain why the final expression is divisible by 3.

Exam practice

1. n is an integer greater than 1

   Prove that $n^2 - n$ is an even number. **(2 marks)**

   > Factorise, then use properties of odd and even numbers.

2. Prove algebraically that the sum of the squares of three consecutive odd numbers is one less than a multiple of 12 **(5 marks)**

   > **⚠ Examiner's hint**
   >
   > Every proof question should finish with a conclusion stating what you have proven.

3. Here are the first five terms of an arithmetic sequence.

   $$11 \quad 8 \quad 5 \quad 2 \quad -1$$

   Meg chooses two terms in the sequence. She squares one of them, and adds the result to the other one.

   Prove that her answer must be a multiple of 3 **(6 marks)**

   > **⚙ Problem solved!**
   >
   > You need to show that this is true for **any** two terms in the sequence. Find an expression for the nth term, then use two different letters to represent two different values of n.

REVISION GUIDE 54, 55

Estimating gradients

What's it all about?

You can estimate the gradient of a curve at a given point by drawing a **tangent** to the curve at that point.

1 On a **distance–time** graph, the gradient at a given point represents the **speed**.

2 On a **velocity–time** graph, the gradient at a given point represents the **acceleration**.

This distance–time graph shows a runner accelerating at the start of a race:

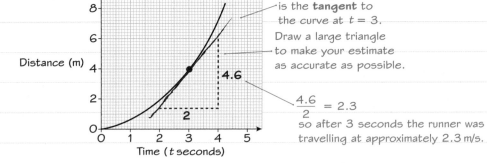

This straight line is the **tangent** to the curve at $t = 3$.

Draw a large triangle to make your estimate as accurate as possible.

$\dfrac{4.6}{2} = 2.3$

so after 3 seconds the runner was travelling at approximately 2.3 m/s.

Worked example

This graph shows the voltage across a phone battery as it charges from empty.

(a) Work out the average rate of increase of voltage between $t = 0$ and $t = 30$.   **(2 marks)**

$\dfrac{3.6}{30} = 0.12$ volts/minute

Amir wants to stop charging his phone when the rate of increase of voltage drops to this average level.

(b) After how long should Amir stop charging his phone? You must show how you got your answer.   **(2 marks)**

10 minutes

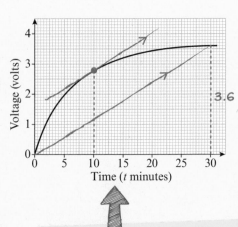

The **average** rate of change between two points is the gradient of a straight line drawn between those two points.

⚠ Examiner's hint

Use a transparent ruler to find the point on the curve where the tangent is **parallel** to the first line.

38

Exam practice

The graph shows the speed in m/s of a robotic vacuum cleaner, t seconds after it begins cleaning a room.

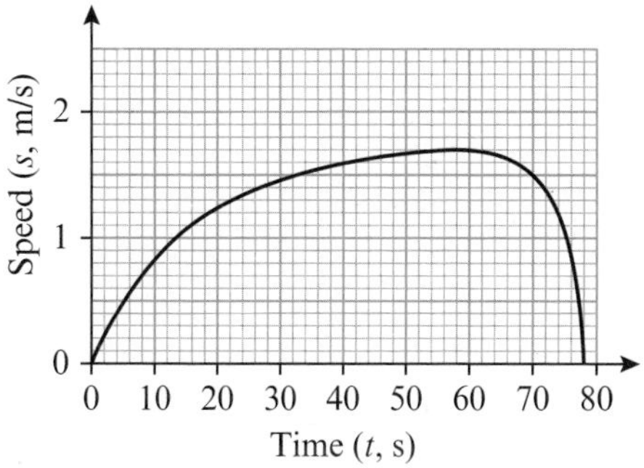

Speed (s, m/s) vs Time (t, s)

This is a **speed–time** graph. The vacuum cleaner starts moving at $t = 0$ and stops moving at $t = 78$

(a) Ciaran says that 58 seconds after it begins cleaning the room, the vacuum cleaner is stationary for a moment.

Explain why Ciaran is incorrect.   **(2 marks)**

....

....

Draw a tangent to the curve at $t = 20$ and find its gradient.

(b) Calculate an estimate for the gradient of the graph when $t = 20$. You must show how you get your answer.

(3 marks)

💡 **Knowledge check**

To find the gradient of a line, draw a triangle and calculate $\dfrac{\text{distance up}}{\text{distance across}}$

⚠ **Examiner's hint**

When calculating gradients, draw as large a triangle as possible. This will improve the accuracy of your calculation.

....

(c) State what your answer to part (b) represents.   **(1 mark)**

....

(d) Explain why your answer to part (b) is only an estimate.

(1 mark)

....

....

⚠ **Examiner's hint**

In part (d) you can refer to the process by which you found your answer.

56

Areas under curves

What's it all about?

You can estimate the area under a curve by drawing trapeziums under the graph.

Area of A = $\frac{1}{2}$(9 + 6) × 1 = 7.5

Area of B = $\frac{1}{2}$(6 + 3) × 1 = 4.5

Area of C = $\frac{1}{2}$(3 + 6) × 1 = 4.5

So an estimate for the area under the curve between $x = 1$ and $x = 4$ is

7.5 + 4.5 + 4.5 = 16.5

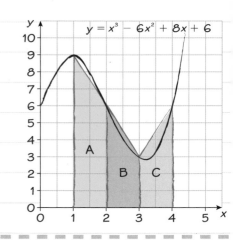

Worked example

This velocity–time graph shows part of a rollercoaster ride.

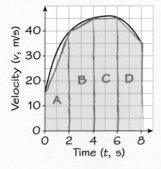

(a) Use four equal intervals on the graph to estimate the total distance travelled by the rollercoaster between $t = 0$ and $t = 8$ **(4 marks)**

$\frac{1}{2}$(15 + 40) × 2 + $\frac{1}{2}$(40 + 45) × 2

+ $\frac{1}{2}$(45 + 45) × 2 + $\frac{1}{2}$(45 + 35) × 2

= 55 + 85 + 90 + 80 = 310 m

(b) Is your answer to part (a) an overestimate or an underestimate? Justify your answer. **(1 mark)**

Underestimate. Every trapezium is completely underneath the curve.

Everything in red is part of the answer.

The area under a velocity–time graph tells you the distance travelled. Divide the area into four equal intervals and draw trapeziums.
If you label your trapeziums it will make your working clearer.
The formula for the area of a trapezium is Area = $\frac{1}{2}$(a + b)h
It's easiest to think of the **width** of the trapezium as h and a and b as the heights of the endpoints.

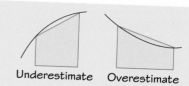

Underestimate   Overestimate

Exam practice

Here is a speed–time graph for a cyclist on a hilly road.

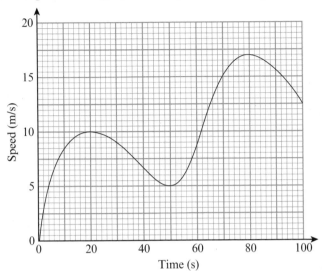

Time (s)

> The area under a speed–time graph between two times represents the distance travelled between those times.

(a) Work out an estimate for the distance travelled by the cyclist in the first 80 seconds. Use four strips of equal width. **(4 marks)**

Knowledge check

The area of a trapezium is given by:

$\frac{1}{2}(a + b)h$

.... m

(b) Tick the box that best describes your answer to part (a). **(1 mark)**

☐ Definitely an underestimate

☐ Definitely an overestimate

☐ Not clear whether it is an underestimate or an overestimate

(c) Explain your answer to part (b). **(1 mark)**

....

....

Examiner's hint

Make sure you show enough working to demonstrate your method. The safest way to do this is to draw and label your trapeziums neatly on the graph.

9,
31

Using algebra

What's it all about?

If you are aiming for a top grade you need to be able to construct and solve your own equations to solve problems.

Worked example

Given that $x : x - 1 = 3x + 2 : 2x$, find the possible values of x.   **(5 marks)**

$$\frac{x}{x - 1} = \frac{3x + 2}{2x}$$

$$2x^2 = (3x + 2)(x - 1)$$

$$2x^2 = 3x^2 - x - 2$$

$$0 = x^2 - x - 2$$

$$0 = (x + 1)(x - 2)$$

$$x = -1 \text{ or } x = 2$$

Use the equivalent ratios to form a quadratic equation.

 Examiner's hint

The question says 'values', so your answer should not just be a single value.

Recurring decimals

You can use algebra to convert a recurring decimal into a fraction:

Write the recurring decimal as n. ➡ Multiply by 10, 100 or 1000. ➡ Subtract to remove the recurring part. ➡ Divide by 9, 99 or 999 to write as a fraction.

Worked example

Prove that the recurring decimal $0.\dot{2}\dot{4}$ has the value $\frac{8}{33}$ **(2 marks)**

Let $n = 0.242\,424\,24\ldots$

$100n = 24.242\,424\,24\ldots$

$- n = -0.242\,424\,24\ldots$

$99n = 24$

$n = \frac{24}{99} = \frac{8}{33}$

Write the recurring decimal as n. There are two recurring digits so multiply n by 100. When you subtract n, the recurring part disappears.

Exam practice

1. The area of rectangle $ABCD$ is $99\,m^2$.

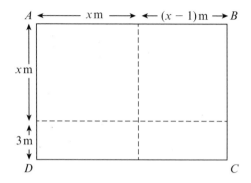

(a) Show that $2x^2 + 5x = 102$ **(3 marks)**

(b) Hence find the perimeter of the rectangle.   **(3 marks)**

....

2. Show that the recurring decimal $0.1\dot{3}\dot{6}$ can be written in the form $\frac{a}{b}$, where a and b are integers with no common factors.   **(3 marks)**

60, 61

Ratio and proportion

What's it all about?

You might need to solve problems involving ratios. Here are three strategies that can help:

1 Equivalent ratios

You can convert equivalent ratios into equations involving fractions:

If $a:b = c:d$ you can write: $\frac{a}{b} = \frac{c}{d}$ or $\frac{a}{c} = \frac{b}{d}$

2 Representing one part

You can use an unknown to represent one part of a ratio. If two quantities are in the ratio $a:b$, you can write them as ax and bx for some value of x.

3 Comparing quantities

If two quantities P and Q are in the ratio $a:b$, then $bP = aQ$.
For example, in this line if $AB:BC = 5:2$, then $2AB = 5BC$

A   B   C

Worked example

In a sports club:
- the ratio of adults to children is $2:1$
- the ratio of women to men is $9:11$
- the ratio of girls to boys is $3:7$

Work out what fraction of all members are female.

(4 marks)

$\frac{2}{3}$ of all members are adults

$\frac{9}{20} \times \frac{2}{3} = \frac{3}{10}$ are women

$\frac{3}{10} \times \frac{1}{3} = \frac{1}{10}$ are girls

$\frac{3}{10} + \frac{1}{10} = \frac{2}{5}$ are female

Knowledge check

If the ratio of adults to children is $2:1$, then $\frac{2}{3}$ of the members are adults and $\frac{1}{3}$ are children.

RATIO & PROPORTION

Exam practice

1. Rory has x bananas and Ed has y bananas. They each eat a banana. The numbers of bananas they each have are now in the ratio $3:2$

   Ed then gives Rory 3 bananas. The numbers of bananas they each have are now in the ratio $3:1$

   Find x and y. You must show all your working. **(5 marks)**

Problem solved!

Use strategy 1 on page 44 to write two equations involving x and y. You can solve these simultaneously to find x and y.

$x = \dots\dots\dots$

$y = \dots\dots\dots$

2. These two rectangles have the same perimeter.

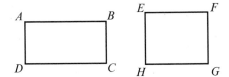

$AB:BC = 11:4$
$EF:FG = 5:4$

Find the ratio $AB:EF$, giving your answer in simplest terms. **(4 marks)**

Problem solved!

Use strategy 3 on page 44 to write the perimeter of the first rectangle in terms of AB, and the perimeter of the second rectangle in terms of EF.

$\dots\dots\dots\dots\dots\dots$

Growth and decay

What's it all about?

Use this formula to solve problems involving **repeated percentage change**:

Amount after n steps = Starting amount × Multiplier^n

Growth

For repeated percentage **increase** the multiplier is greater than 1.

Decay

For repeated percentage **decrease** the multiplier is less than 1.

x_0 is the starting amount

Worked example

A scientist is creating a model for the number of carp in a lake. Her model predicts that $C_{n+1} = 0.8C_n$ where C_n is the number of carp after n years.

(a) Does this model predict that the number of carp is increasing or decreasing each year? **(1 mark)**

Decreasing by 20% each year

(b) $C_0 = 600$. Calculate (i) C_1 (ii) C_3 **(2 marks)**

(i) $C_1 = 0.8 \times C_0 = 0.8 \times 600 = 480$

(ii) $C_2 = 0.8 \times C_1 = 0.8 \times 480 = 384$

$C_3 = 0.8 \times C_2 = 0.8 \times 384 = 307$

(nearest whole number)

(c) This model predicts that after k years the number of carp in the lake will have dropped below 200.

Calculate the value of k. **(2 marks)**

After 4 years:

$C_4 = 0.8^4 \times 600 = 246$ (nearest whole number)

After 5 years:

$C_5 = 0.8^5 \times 600 = 197$ (nearest whole number)

$k = 5$

> This question uses iteration notation. There is more about this on page 30. The values C_0, C_1, C_2 and so on form a sequence that decreases with each term.
>
> $C_n = 0.8^n \times C_0$ → Starting amount
>
> Final amount   Multiplier

Exam practice

1. John invests £2000 in a savings account. The account pays 1.3% per annum compound interest.

   (a) Find the amount in the account after 5 years. **(2 marks)**

£ ....

Una invests £5000 in a different savings account.
This account pays $p\%$ compound interest per annum.
After 6 years, her investment is worth £5615.

   (b) Work out the value of p, correct to 3 significant figures. **(3 marks)**

$p = $ ....

2. At time $t = 0$ a cup of coffee has a temperature of 87 °C. Each minute, the temperature of the coffee reduces by 8%. After t minutes, the temperature is X_t °C. The temperature is modelled by the equations:

$X_0 = j$
$X_{t+1} = kX_t$

   (a) Write the values of the constants j and k. **(2 marks)**

$j = $ ....

$k = $ ....

   (b) Find the value of X_3. **(2 marks)**

$X_3 = $ ....

   (c) Give a reason why this model might not be very accurate for large values of t. **(1 mark)**

....

....

REVISION GUIDE 69, 71

Proportionality formulae

What's it all about?

 When y is directly proportional to x you can write:

- $y \propto x$
- $y = kx$ — k is called the **constant** of proportionality.

2 When y is inversely proportional to x you can write:

- $y \propto \dfrac{1}{x}$
- $y = \dfrac{k}{x}$

You can use these formulae for harder proportionality relationships:

Proportionality in words	Using $\propto$	Formula
y is directly proportional to the square of x	$y \propto x^2$	$y = kx^2$
y is directly proportional to the cube of x	$y \propto x^3$	$y = kx^3$
y is directly proportional to the square root of x	$y \propto \sqrt{x}$	$y = k\sqrt{x}$
y is inversely proportional to the square of x	$y \propto \dfrac{1}{x^2}$	$y = \dfrac{k}{x^2}$

Worked example

y is directly proportional to $\sqrt{x}$
$y = 50$ when $x = 1600$

Find the value of y when $x = 900$ **(3 marks)**

$y = k\sqrt{x}$
$50 = k \times \sqrt{1600}$
$k = 50 \div \sqrt{1600} = 1.25$
$y = 1.25\sqrt{x}$
$\quad = 1.25 \times \sqrt{900}$
$\quad = 37.5$

1. Write a formula using k for the **constant of proportionality.**
2. Use the numbers given in the question to find the value of k.
3. Use your formula to find y when $x = 900$

Exam practice

1. The table shows some values for two variables:

q	8	9	10	11
p	12.8	18.225	25	33.275

$p \propto q^n$ for some integer n.

(a) Find the value of n. Show enough working
to justify your answer. **(3 marks)**

> Try some different
> values of n until you find
> one that fits the data.

> **⚠ Examiner's hint**
>
> You should always show
> working. But when a
> question **specifically**
> asks for it, make sure
> your working is neatly
> laid out and easy
> to read.

$n =$ ....

(b) Find a formula for p in terms of q. **(3 marks)**

....

(c) Find the value of p when $q = 12$ **(1 mark)**

$p =$ ....

> As q increases, p
> increases. Use this fact
> to check your answer
> to part (c).

2. y is directly proportional to b^2
When $y = 15$, $b = 5$
b is inversely proportional to x
When $b = 8$, $x = 10$

Find a formula for y in terms of x. **(5 marks)**

> **⚙ Problem
> solved!**
>
> 1. Find a formula for y
>   in terms of b.
> 2. Find a formula for b
>   in terms of x.
> 3. Substitute your
>   second formula
>   into your first
>   and simplify.

....

77–79

Trigonometry

What's it all about?

Use SOH CAH TOA to remember the three trigonometric ratios for **right-angled** triangles:

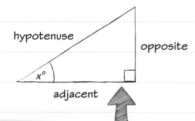

hypotenuse

opposite

$x°$

adjacent

The sides of the triangle are labelled relative to the **angle** you need to find.

Trigonometric ratios

$$\sin x° = \frac{opp}{hyp} \quad \text{(remember this as SOH)}$$

$$\cos x° = \frac{adj}{hyp} \quad \text{(remember this as CAH)}$$

$$\tan x° = \frac{opp}{adj} \quad \text{(remember this as TOA)}$$

Exact values

You need to be able to remember the following exact values of sin, cos and tan **without a calculator**:

	0°	30°	45°	60°	90°
sin	0	$\frac{1}{2}$	$\frac{\sqrt{2}}{2}$	$\frac{\sqrt{3}}{2}$	1
cos	1	$\frac{\sqrt{3}}{2}$	$\frac{\sqrt{2}}{2}$	$\frac{1}{2}$	0
tan	0	$\frac{\sqrt{3}}{3}$	1	$\sqrt{3}$	undefined

Worked example

The table shows values of x and y that satisfy the equation $y = a + b\cos x°$

x	0	45	90
y	5	$3 + \sqrt{2}$	3

Find the exact value of y when $x = 30$.

(4 marks)

$\cos 0° = 1$ so $a + b = 5$

$\cos 90° = 0$ so $a = 3$

$a = 3$ and $b = 2$

So when $x = 30$

$y = a + b\cos 30° = 3 + 2 \times \frac{\sqrt{3}}{2}$

$\qquad\qquad = 3 + \sqrt{3}$

 Problem solved!

You know the exact value of $\cos x°$ when $x = 0$, 45 or 90. Use this to write equations involving a and b.

Once you have found a and b you can substitute $x = 30$ into the equation.

 Examiner's hint

You need to be able to answer a question like this **without** a calculator.

Exam practice

1. In the diagram, **S** is part of a regular 12-sided polygon with sides of length 5 cm.

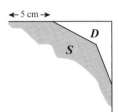

Two perpendicular sides of the polygon have been extended to form a new shape, **D**.

Find the area of **D**. Give your answer correct to 3 significant figures. **(4 marks)**

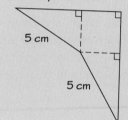
.... cm^2

2. The diagram shows a circle drawn inside a right-angled triangle.

The circle touches all three sides of the triangle.

Find the radius of the circle. Give your answer correct to 3 significant figures. **(4 marks)**

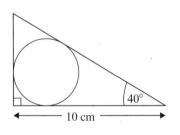

40°

10 cm

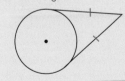
.... cm

99, 100

Sine and cosine rules

You need to learn the **sine rule** and the **cosine rule**. You can use them in any triangle:

Sine rule

$$\frac{a}{\sin A} = \frac{b}{\sin B} = \frac{c}{\sin C}$$

$$\frac{\sin A}{a} = \frac{\sin B}{b} = \frac{\sin C}{c}$$

Cosine rule

$$a^2 = b^2 + c^2 - 2bc\cos A$$

$$\cos A = \frac{b^2 + c^2 - a^2}{2bc}$$

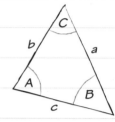

Which rule?

This chart shows you which rule to use when solving trigonometry problems in triangles:

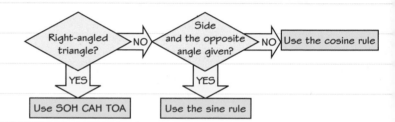

Worked example

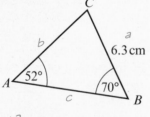

Calculate the length of AC.   **(3 marks)**

$$\frac{b}{\sin B} = \frac{a}{\sin A}$$

$$\frac{AC}{\sin 70°} = \frac{6.3}{\sin 52°}$$

$$AC = \frac{6.3 \times \sin 70°}{\sin 52°}$$

$$= 7.5126\ldots$$

$$= 7.5 \text{ cm (2 s.f.)}$$

> You know one side and its opposite angle, so you can use the sine rule. The version with side lengths on **top** of the fractions is easier to use when you need to find a missing length.

> Everything in red is part of the answer.

Exam practice

1. The diagram shows two triangles *PQR* and *PRS*.

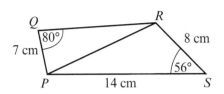

(a) Find the length *PR*. **(3 marks)**

.... cm

(b) Find the size of angle *QRP*. **(3 marks)**

..........................°

2.

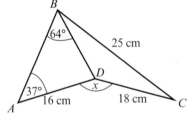

Work out the size of the angle *ADC* marked *x*. Give your answer in degrees to 1 decimal place. **(6 marks)**

..........................°

Examiner's hint

Check whether triangles are right-angled. If they are, you can use SOH CAH TOA. Neither of these triangles is right-angled so you need to use the sine rule and the cosine rule.

For part (a) you know two sides and the included angle. You can use the cosine rule to find *PR*.

Problem solved!

You don't have enough information to work out *x* directly. Look at triangle *ABD* first and see whether you can use this triangle to get more information about triangle *BCD*.

Knowledge check

Angles in a triangle add up to 180° and angles around a point add up to 360°.

84

Sectors of circles

What's it all about?

You can find the area of a sector and the length of an arc by thinking of them as fractions of a circle.

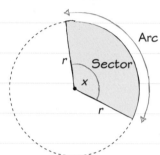

Arc

Sector

For a sector with angle x of a circle with radius r:

$$\text{Sector} = \frac{x}{360°} \text{ of the whole circle so}$$

$$\text{Area of sector} = \frac{x}{360°} \times \pi r^2$$

$$\text{Arc length} = \frac{x}{360°} \times 2\pi r$$

Worked example

AB is a chord of a circle with centre O and radius $6\,cm$.

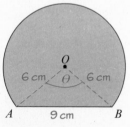

A 9 cm B

$AB = 9\,cm$

Find the perimeter of the shaded shape. **(5 marks)**

$$\cos\theta = \frac{6^2 + 6^2 - 9^2}{2 \times 6 \times 6}$$

$$= -\frac{1}{8}$$

$$\theta = 97.1807\ldots°$$

$$\text{Arc } AB = \frac{360 - 97.1807\ldots}{360} \times 2 \times \pi \times 6$$

$$= 27.5084\ldots$$

Perimeter $= 27.5084\ldots + 9 = 36.5\,cm$ (3 s.f.)

Always read the question carefully. You need to find the **perimeter** here. This will be the sum of the arc AB and the straight line AB.

Everything in red is part of the answer.

⚠ **Examiner's hint**

Don't round any values until the end of your calculation. Use the memory functions on your calculator or write down at least 4 d.p.

Exam practice

1. The diagram shows an earring in the shape of an outline of a sector of a circle.

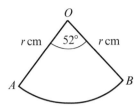

The perimeter is made from a single piece of wire of length 10 cm.

Find the radius of the circle, r. **(4 marks)**

> **⚠ Examiner's hint**
>
> Check that your answers make sense. The diagram isn't to scale but it should look about right. If the overall perimeter is 10 cm the value of r should be approximately 3 or 4

> Remember to include the two radii when you are writing an expression for the perimeter.

.... cm

2. In the diagram, ABC is the sector of a circle with radius 12 cm and centre A.

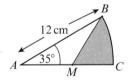

M is the midpoint of AC.

Find the area of the shaded shape MBC. **(4 marks)**

> **💡 Knowledge check**
>
> You can use $\frac{1}{2} \times$ base $\times$ height to find the area of any triangle.
>
> Use trigonometry to find the height of the triangle.
>
>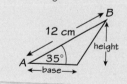

.... cm²

Triangles and segments

What's it all about?

You can use this formula to find the area of **any triangle** if you know the lengths of two sides and the angle between them:

$$\text{Area} = \frac{1}{2} ab \sin C$$

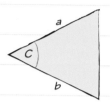

Areas of segments

A chord divides a circle into two **segments**.

| Area of minor segment | = | Area of whole sector | − | Area of triangle |

Worked example

The diagram shows a sector of a circle with centre O.

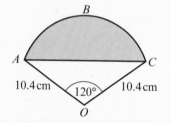

Work out the area of the shaded segment ABC.
Give your answer correct to 3 significant figures. **(5 marks)**

Whole sector $OABC$:

$$\text{Area} = \frac{120}{360} \times \pi \times 10.4^2$$

$$= 113.2648\ldots \text{cm}^2$$

Triangle OAC:

$$\text{Area} = \frac{1}{2} \times 10.4 \times 10.4 \times \sin 120°$$

$$= 46.8346\ldots \text{cm}^2$$

Shaded segment ABC:

$$\text{Area} = 113.2648\ldots - 46.8346\ldots$$

$$= 66.4302\ldots$$

$$= 66.4 \text{cm}^2 \text{ (to 3 s.f.)}$$

If you are aiming for a top grade you need to be able to calculate the area of a sector and a triangle.

To get full marks you need to keep track of your working. Make sure you write down exactly what you are calculating at each step.

Remember that 10.4 cm is the length of one side of the triangle **and** the radius of the circle.

Make sure you don't round too soon. Write down all the figures from your calculator display at each step. Only round your **final answer** to 3 significant figures.

Exam practice

1. The diagram shows a shape *ABCD* made from a triangle and a sector of a circle with centre *A* and radius 2.3 m.

BC is parallel to *AD*.

Find the area of the shape.

(5 marks)

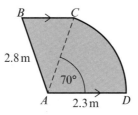

Knowledge check

Alternate angles in parallel lines are equal:

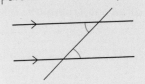

Problem solved!

Use the sine rule to find the size of the angles in triangle *ABC*, then use the formula for the area of any triangle.

.... m²

2. In the diagram

AB is an arc of a circle radius *r* and centre *C*

AC is an arc of a circle radius *r* and centre *B*

BC is an arc of a circle radius *r* and centre *A*

Prove that the area of the shaded shape

is $\frac{1}{2}r^2(\pi - \sqrt{3})$

(5 marks)

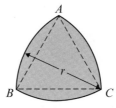

The radii of the three arcs are the same, so *ABC* is an equilateral triangle.

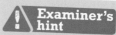

Examiner's hint

You should be able to answer this question without a calculator using exact trigonometric ratios.

76, 102

3D lengths and angles

You can find missing lengths and angles in 3D shapes by considering different triangles. For example:

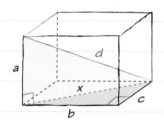

$$x^2 = b^2 + c^2$$

$$d^2 = a^2 + x^2$$
$$= a^2 + b^2 + c^2$$

Lines and planes

If you can construct a right-angled triangle you can use SOH CAH TOA to find the angle between a line and a plane.

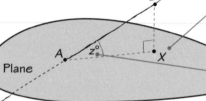

Plane

Point X is directly below point B, so ABX is a right-angled triangle.

Angle z is the angle between the line and the plane.

Worked example

Here is a cuboid.

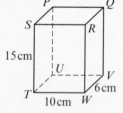

15 cm

6 cm

10 cm

Find the size of angle PWU. **(5 marks)**

$UW^2 = UT^2 + TW^2 = 6^2 + 10^2$

$UW = \sqrt{136}$

$PW^2 = UW^2 + PU^2 = 136 + 15^2$

$PW = \sqrt{361} = 19$

$\cos \angle PWU = \dfrac{\sqrt{136}}{19} = 0.6137\ldots$

$\angle PWU = 52.1°$ (3 s.f.)

⬅ **Knowledge check** Use 2D Pythagoras to find the length of UW:
$UW^2 = UT^2 + TW^2$

⬅ PWU is a right-angled triangle, so you only need to find two lengths to calculate angle PWU.

⬅ $\cos x = \dfrac{adj}{hyp}$

Exam practice

1. The diagram shows a cuboid.
$AB = 14\,\text{m}$ and $BC = 22\,\text{m}$.

The diagonal $FC = 27\,\text{m}$.

Calculate the volume of
the cuboid.   **(3 marks)**

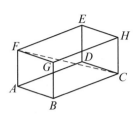

> **Examiner's hint**
>
> When you work out the height of the cuboid, leave your answer as a square or a surd to avoid a rounding error.

.... m^3

2. The diagram shows a square-based pyramid.

The vertex of the pyramid X is
8 cm above the midpoint of AC.

Find the size of angle AXC.
Give your answer to one
decimal place.   **(5 marks)**

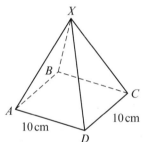

> Find the length AC using Pythagoras' theorem, then sketch triangle ACX.

> **Examiner's hint**
>
> Read the question carefully and make sure you know which angle you are trying to find. Angle AXC is at the **top** of the pyramid.

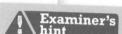

......................°

REVISION GUIDE 89, 90

Transformations

What's it all about?

You can describe two or more transformations using a single transformation.

A rotation 90° anticlockwise about O followed by a reflection in the x-axis is the same as a single reflection in the line $y = -x$

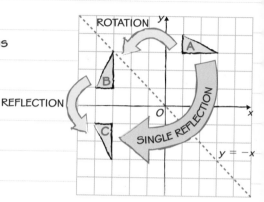

ROTATION

REFLECTION

SINGLE REFLECTION

$y = -x$

Invariant points

A point that remains the same after a transformation is called an **invariant** point.

Shape **A** has been rotated by 180°. (3, 2) is an invariant point. (3, 1) is not an invariant point as it is transformed to (3, 3).

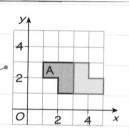

Worked example

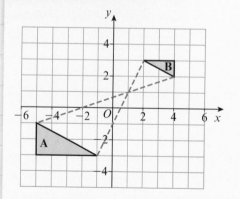

Describe fully the single transformation that maps triangle **A** onto triangle **B**. **(2 marks)**

Enlargement scale factor $-\frac{1}{2}$, centre (1, 1)

The side lengths on **B** are half the side lengths on **A**. **B** is on the other side of the centre of enlargement, and upside down, so the scale factor is $-\frac{1}{2}$. Draw lines between corresponding points on **A** and **B**. The point where these intersect is the centre of enlargement.

Exam practice

1.

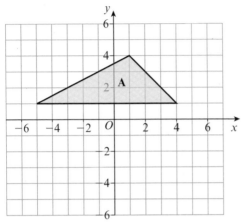

On the grid, enlarge triangle **A** by a scale factor of $-\frac{1}{3}$ with centre of enlargement $(-2, -2)$.

Label your image **B**. **(2 marks)**

> Draw lines from the vertices of **A** through the centre of enlargement. The vertices on **B** will lie on these lines, on the other side of $(-2, -2)$. The lengths of the sides of **B** will be $\frac{1}{3}$ of the lengths of the corresponding sides on **A**.

2.

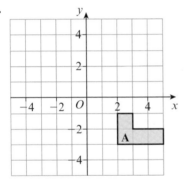

Shape **A** is transformed by a translation with vector $\begin{pmatrix} -4 \\ 2 \end{pmatrix}$ followed by a rotation of 180° about the point $(1, -1)$. One point on **A** is invariant under this combined transformation.

Find the coordinates of this point. **(2 marks)**

> 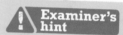 **Examiner's hint**
>
> You can show your working by drawing both transformations on the grid.

> An invariant point has to be the **same** point on the object as it is on the image.

> **Knowledge check**
>
> $\begin{pmatrix} -4 \\ 2 \end{pmatrix}$ means move 4 places left and 2 places up.

(.................., ...)

96

Congruent triangles

What's it all about?

You have to show that **one** of these four conditions is true to prove that two triangles are congruent:

1 **SSS** (three sides are equal)

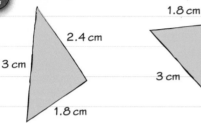

2.4 cm
1.8 cm
3 cm
2.4 cm
3 cm
1.8 cm

2 **AAS** (two angles and a corresponding side are equal)

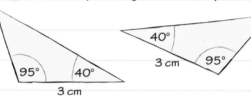

95° 40°
3 cm
40° 95°
3 cm

3 **SAS** (two sides and the included angle are equal)

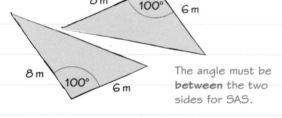

8 m 100° 6 m
8 m 100° 6 m

The angle must be **between** the two sides for SAS.

4 **RHS** (right angle, hypotenuse and a side are equal)

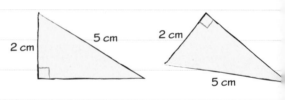

2 cm
5 cm
2 cm
5 cm

Worked example

ABCD and *DEFG* are squares.

Prove that triangles *AGD* and *ECD* are congruent. **(4 marks)**

AD = DC (two sides of same square)
DE = DG (two sides of same square)
∠CDE = ∠CDG + 90°
∠GDA = ∠CDG + 90°
So ∠CDE = ∠GDA
So AGD is congruent to ECD (SAS)

Don't start by assuming the triangles are congruent. You need to use the properties of the two **squares** to show that one of the four conditions of congruency is satisfied.

Exam practice

1. The diagram shows a parallelogram $ABEF$ and a square $BCDE$.

Prove that $AC = FD$.

(5 marks)

Problem solved!

You can do this using congruent triangles. Start by proving that triangle ABC is congruent to triangle FED.

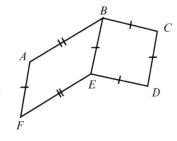

2. Triangle ABE is an isosceles triangle, with base AB.

Angle EAD = Angle CBE.

(a) Prove that triangle ADE is congruent to triangle BCE.

(4 marks)

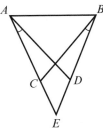

If you have to prove that two triangles are congruent look for **common sides** or **common angles** in both triangles. Angle AEB is common to both triangles so it must be equal.

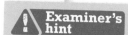

Examiner's hint

Make sure you state which condition of congruency you have shown.

(b) Hence prove that $AC = BD$. **(2 marks)**

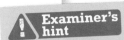

Examiner's hint

'Hence' means you can use your answer to part (a).

Similar shapes 1

What's it all about?

Shapes are **similar** if one is an enlargement of the other. In similar shapes **corresponding sides** are in the same ratio, and **corresponding angles** are equal.

Similar triangles

Two triangles are similar if they satisfy any **one** of these conditions:

 Two pairs of angles are equal

 All three pairs of sides are in the same ratio

③ Two sides are in the same ratio and the included angles are equal.

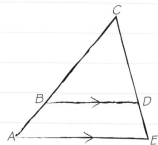

Angle CBD = Angle CAE

Angle CDB = Angle CEA

(corresponding angles in parallel lines)

So triangle BCD is similar to triangle ACE (two pairs of angles are equal).

Worked example

XYZ and *ABC* are similar triangles.

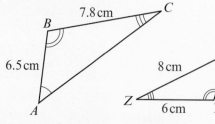

(a) Work out the length of *AC*. **(2 marks)**

$$\frac{AC}{XZ} = \frac{BC}{YZ}$$

$$\frac{AC}{8} = \frac{7.8}{6}$$

$$AC = \frac{7.8 \times 8}{6}$$

$$= 10.4 \text{ cm}$$

(b) Work out the length of *XY*. **(2 marks)**

$$\frac{XY}{AB} = \frac{YZ}{BC}$$

$$\frac{XY}{6.5} = \frac{6}{7.8}$$

$$XY = \frac{6 \times 6.5}{7.8}$$

$$= 5 \text{ cm}$$

Similar triangles will not always be shown in the same orientation. Make sure you are comparing **corresponding sides** when you do any calculations. Look at the matching angles to determine which sides are corresponding.

Exam practice

1. In the diagram, ABC and ADE are straight lines.
   $AB:BC = 3:2$ and
   $AD:DE = 3:2$

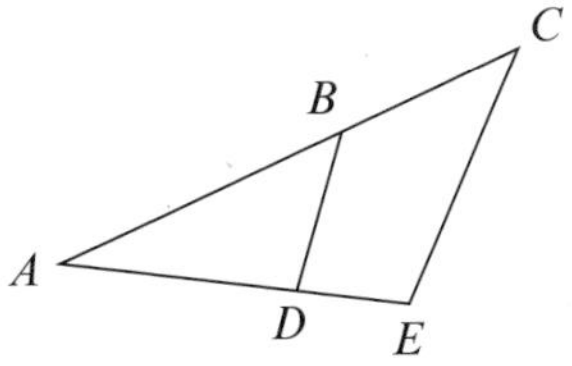

   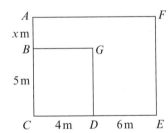

   (a) Explain why triangle ABD and triangle ACE are similar. **(3 marks)**

   ....

   ....

   ....

   $BC = 7$ cm and $BD = 6$ cm.

   (b) Find the length of CE. **(2 marks)**

   .... cm

2. The two rectangles shown in the diagram are similar. There are two possible values of x.

   Work out each of these values.
   (5 marks)

   (diagram: rectangle with corners A, F, B, G, C, D, E; x m, 5 m, 4 m, 6 m labelled)

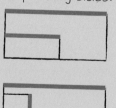
   $x =$ ....

   $x =$ ....

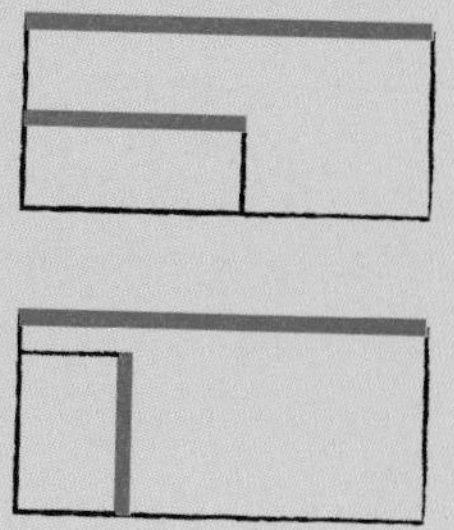

Similar shapes 2

What's it all about?

Similar solids are enlargements of each other. If the **linear** scale factor of the enlargement is k:

- lengths are multiplied by k
- surface areas are multiplied by k^2
- volumes are multiplied by k^3

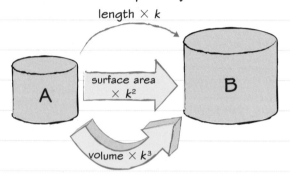

length × k

surface area × k^2

A

B

volume × k^3

Ratios

If lengths in two similar solids are in the ratio $a:b$ then

 surface areas will be in the ratio $a^2:b^2$

 volumes will be in the ratio $a^3:b^3$

Worked example

These two steel prisms are similar.

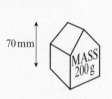
70 mm
MASS 200 g

MASS 3125 g

Start by writing the relationship in terms of k^3. Find k using the ∛☐ button on your calculator, then multiply the height of the small prism by k.

(a) Work out the height of the larger prism. **(3 marks)**

$200 \times k^3 = 3125$

$k^3 = 15.625$

$k = 2.5$

Enlarged height = $70 \times 2.5 = 175$ mm

(b) Work out the ratio of the surface areas of the two prisms. **(2 marks)**

Ratio of lengths = $1:2.5$

Ratio of surface areas = $1:6.25$

$= 4:25$

You can leave your ratio in terms of decimals, or find an equivalent ratio with whole numbers.

Exam practice

1. These two sculptures are mathematically similar.

A   **B**

The surface area of **A** is $6480\,\text{cm}^2$
The surface area of **B** is $2000\,\text{cm}^2$
The volume of **A** is $1458\,\text{cm}^3$

Find the volume of **B**.   **(3 marks)**

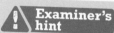

Use the surface areas given to find the area scale factor, k^2.

> **⚠ Examiner's hint**
>
> Check that your answers make sense. Sculpture **B** is smaller than sculpture **A** so it will have a smaller volume.

.... cm^3

2. Solids **A**, **B**, and **C** are similar.

The ratio of the volume of **A** to the volume of **B** is $27:64$
The ratio of the height of **B** to the height of **C** is $6:7$

Find the ratio of the surface area of **A** to the surface area of **C**.

Give your answer in the form $p : q$, where p and q are integers.   **(4 marks)**

> **⚙ Problem solved!**
>
> Work step by step.
> 1. Find the ratio of the height of **A** to the height of **B**.
> 2. Find suitable equivalent ratios, or use multipliers, to find the ratio of the height of **A** to the height of **C**.
> 3. Square this ratio, then find an equivalent ratio using integers.

....

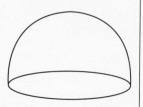
85, 86

Volume and surface area

What's it all about?

If you need to use the formulae for surface areas or volumes of cones or spheres, they will be given to you with the question.

You need to learn these formulae for cylinders and prisms:

Cylinder

Volume = $\pi r^2 h$

Surface area = $2\pi r^2 + 2\pi rh$

Prism

Volume = area of cross-section × length

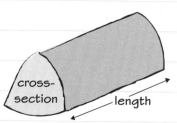

cross-section

length

Worked example

A paperweight is made in the shape of a solid hemisphere.

> Volume of sphere = $\frac{4}{3}\pi r^3$
>
> Surface area of sphere = $4\pi r^2$

> Find an expression in terms of r for the total surface area. Remember to include the base.

The total surface area of the hemisphere is 75π cm².

Find the exact volume of the hemisphere. Give your answer in terms of π.

> Use the [S⇔D] button on your calculator to convert between decimals and answers in terms of π.

Surface area = $\pi r^2 + \frac{1}{2}(4\pi r^2)$

$\qquad = 3\pi r^2$

$\qquad 75\pi = 3\pi r^2$ so $r = 5$

Volume = $\frac{1}{2}\left(\frac{4}{3}\pi \times 5^3\right) = \frac{250}{3}\pi$ cm³

Exam practice

1. The diagram shows the frustum of a cone.

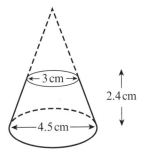

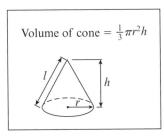

Volume of cone $= \frac{1}{3}\pi r^2 h$

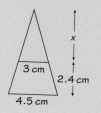
It is made by removing a cone of base diameter 3 cm from a cone of base diameter 4.5 cm. The frustum is 2.4 cm tall.

Find the volume of the frustum. **(4 marks)**

.... cm³

2. A cylindrical log of radius 20 cm and length 1.2 m is floating in water.

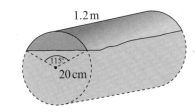

The waterline makes an angle of 115° at the centre of the circle, as shown in the diagram.

Find the volume of the submerged section of the log.

(3 marks)

The submerged section of the log is a prism, whose cross-section is a segment of a circle.

Make sure your units are consistent before using a formula. Choose m or cm and give units with your answer.

....

104, 105

Using circle theorems

What's it all about?

You need to learn these six circle facts and theorems.

1 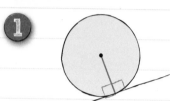 A tangent to a circle makes a right angle with the radius.

2  Opposite angles in a cyclic quadrilateral add up to 180°.

3 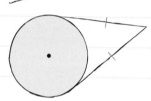 Tangents that meet at a point are the same length.

4 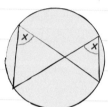 Angles subtended in the same segment are equal.

5 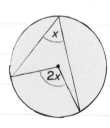 Angle at the centre of a circle is twice the angle at the circumference.

6   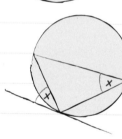 Angle between a tangent and a chord is equal to the angle in the alternate segment.

Worked example

The diagram shows a circle with centre O.
AB and AC are tangents to the circle, and angle $BDC = 48°$.

Find the size of angle BAC. **(4 marks)**

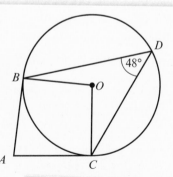

$\angle BOC = 96°$ (angle at the centre of a circle is twice the angle at the circumference)

$\angle OBA = \angle OCA = 90°$ (tangent is perpendicular to radius at the point of contact)

So $\angle BAC + 90° + 90° + 96° = 360°$

$\angle BAC = 84°$

💡 **Knowledge check**

The angles in a quadrilateral add up to 360°.

Exam practice

1. *A*, *B*, *C* and *D* are points on the circumference of a circle. *EF* is a tangent to the circle.

    Find the size of angle *BCD*.
    (4 marks)

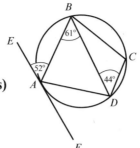

If you can spot a tangent (like *EF*) and a chord (like *AB*), then there is a good chance you can use the alternate segment theorem.

ABCD is a cyclic quadrilateral.

> **⚠ Examiner's hint**
>
> Make sure you give reasons for each stage of your working, and use the correct mathematical language.

........................°

2. *A*, *B*, *C* and *D* are points on the circumference of a circle. *PAB* and *PCD* are straight lines.

    (a) Prove that triangles *PBC* and *PDA* are similar.   **(4 marks)**

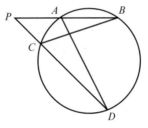

> **⚙ Problem solved!**
>
> You can use the fact that angles subtended in the same segment are equal.

Make sure you state which condition of similar triangles has been satisfied.

(b) Hence show that *PA* × *PB* = *PC* × *PD*.   **(2 marks)**

Proving circle theorems

What's it all about?

You need to be able to **prove** the circle theorems. You can do this using standard circle facts about tangents and radii, and standard angle facts involving angles in triangles.

What can you assume?

 You should **never** assume the result you are trying to prove.

 Read the question carefully – you might be told other facts or theorems you are **not** allowed to use.

Worked example

AC is a diameter of the circle with centre O.

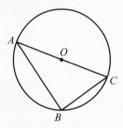

Prove that angle $ABC = 90°$. You may **not** use any circle theorems in your proof.　　　**(4 marks)**

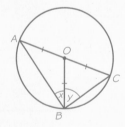

$OA = OB = OC$ because they are all radii
$\angle OAB = x$ and $\angle OCB = y$ (base angles of an isosceles triangle are equal)
So $x + x + y + y = 180°$ (angles in triangle ABC add up to $180°$)
$2x + 2y = 180°$
　$x + y = 90°$
So angle $ABC = 90°$

You are told not to use any circle theorems in your proof, so you need to use angle facts about straight lines and triangles.

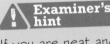 **Problem solved!**

Any radii of the same circle must be the same length. This means triangles AOB and BOC are isosceles.

⚠ **Examiner's hint**

If you are neat and clear, you can show working by drawing a sketch or annotating the one given in the question.

Exam practice

1. A, B and D are points on the circumference of a circle, centre O. AC is a tangent to the circle. Angle $ABD = x$ and angle $DAC = y$.

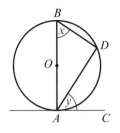

(a) Prove that $x = y$. You may **not** use the alternate segment theorem in your proof. **(3 marks)**

> You can use the fact that the angle in a semicircle is 90°.

Neil says that this proof is a proof of the alternate segment theorem.

(b) State, with a reason, whether Neil is correct. **(2 marks)**

....

....

> To prove something you need to show that it is true in every case. Look at your answer to part (a). Would it work for every case of the alternate segment theorem?

2. A, B and C are points on the circumference of a circle, centre O.

Prove that the size of angle AOC is twice the size of angle ABC. **(4 marks)**

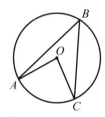

> This is a standard circle theorem, but here you are asked to prove it. Do not assume that it is true anywhere in your working. You need to use facts about triangles to show that it is true.

Problem solved!

> Draw a straight line through OB and extend it past O.

Vectors

What's it all about?

These three techniques are useful for solving vector problems:

1 Two vectors are parallel if one is a **scalar multiple** of the other:

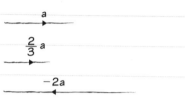

$$\text{———} \quad a$$

$$\frac{2}{3}a$$

$$-2a$$

2 If point M divides PQ in the **ratio** $a:b$, then

$$\overrightarrow{PM} = \frac{a}{a+b}\overrightarrow{PQ}$$

3 If **two** of the vectors $\overrightarrow{AB}$, $\overrightarrow{BC}$ or $\overrightarrow{AC}$ are parallel, then A, B and C are **colinear** (lie on the same straight line).

> $PR:RQ = 1:2$ There are $2 + 1 = 3$ parts in this ratio. This means that R is $\frac{1}{3}$ of the way along PQ so $\overrightarrow{PR} = \frac{1}{3}\overrightarrow{PQ}$
> $OR:OS = 1:3$ This means that $\overrightarrow{OS} = 3\overrightarrow{OR}$

> To show that T, P and S lie on the same straight line you need to show that **two** of the vectors $\overrightarrow{TP}$, $\overrightarrow{TS}$ and $\overrightarrow{PS}$ are parallel.

Worked example

In the diagram, OPQ is a triangle. Point R lies on the line PQ such that $PR:RQ = 1:2$ Point S lies on the line through OR such that $OR:OS = 1:3$

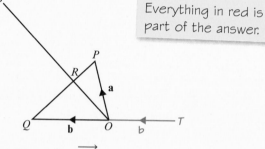

> Everything in red is part of the answer.

(a) Show that $\overrightarrow{OS} = 2\mathbf{a} + \mathbf{b}$ **(3 marks)**

$$\overrightarrow{PQ} = -\mathbf{a} + \mathbf{b}, \text{ so } \overrightarrow{PR} = \frac{1}{3}(-\mathbf{a} + \mathbf{b})$$

$$\overrightarrow{OR} = \mathbf{a} + \frac{1}{3}(-\mathbf{a} + \mathbf{b})$$

$$= \frac{1}{3}(2\mathbf{a} + \mathbf{b})$$

$$\overrightarrow{OS} = 3\overrightarrow{OR}$$

$$= 2\mathbf{a} + \mathbf{b}$$

(b) Point T is added to the diagram such that $\overrightarrow{TO} = \mathbf{b}$. Prove that points T, P and S lie on the same straight line.   **(3 marks)**

$$\overrightarrow{TP} = \mathbf{a} + \mathbf{b}$$

$$\overrightarrow{TS} = \mathbf{b} + 2\mathbf{a} + \mathbf{b}$$

$$= 2\mathbf{a} + 2\mathbf{b}$$

$$= 2(\mathbf{a} + \mathbf{b})$$

$\overrightarrow{TS} = 2\overrightarrow{TP}$ so $\overrightarrow{TS}$ and $\overrightarrow{TP}$ are parallel. Both vectors pass through T so T, P and S lie on the same straight line.

Exam practice

1. In the diagram, M is the midpoint of OA and N divides OC in the ratio $1:2$

   Point B lies on AN.

   $\overrightarrow{OM} = \mathbf{a}$ and $\overrightarrow{ON} = \mathbf{b}$

   $\overrightarrow{MB} = \frac{1}{5}\overrightarrow{MC}$ and $\overrightarrow{AB} = k\overrightarrow{AN}$

   Find the value of k.   **(4 marks)**

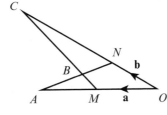

> **Knowledge check**
>
> You can trace a path around a shape adding vectors as you go.

> Find $\overrightarrow{AB}$ and $\overrightarrow{AN}$ in terms of $\mathbf{a}$ and $\mathbf{b}$.

$k = $ ....

2. $ABCD$ is a square.

   P divides AB in the ratio $4:1$ and Q divides DC in the ratio $2:3$. M is the midpoint of AD, and N is the midpoint of MC.

   Prove that P, N and Q lie on the same straight line.   **(4 marks)**

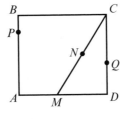

> **Knowledge check**
>
> If $\mathbf{a}$ is a vector then $-\mathbf{a}$ is a parallel vector with the same magnitude and an opposite direction.

> **Problem solved!**
>
> You need to show that **two** of the vectors $\overrightarrow{PN}$, $\overrightarrow{PQ}$ or $\overrightarrow{NQ}$ are parallel.

Let $\overrightarrow{AB} = \mathbf{a}$ and $\overrightarrow{AD} = \mathbf{b}$

77, 98, 105

Geometry and algebra

What's it all about?

Make sure you are confident using geometric facts to form and solve your own equations. Here are three top tips:

 1 Lengths and angles must be **positive** numbers. You might need to reject negative answers.

 2 Read the question carefully to work out what you are being asked to find.

 3 Make sure you are confident rearranging algebraic fractions and solving quadratic equations.

Worked example

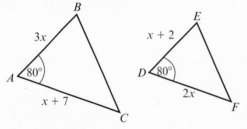

Triangle ABC is similar to triangle DEF.

Work out the ratio of the area of triangle ABC to the area of triangle DEF. **(5 marks)**

$$\frac{x+7}{2x} = \frac{3x}{x+2}$$
$$(x+7)(x+2) = 6x^2$$
$$x^2 + 9x + 14 = 6x^2$$
$$5x^2 - 9x - 14 = 0$$
$$(5x - 14)(x + 1) = 0$$

$x = 2.8$ or $x = -1$

Ratio of lengths $= 3x : x + 2$

$\qquad\qquad\quad = 8.4 : 4.8 = 7 : 4$

Ratio of areas $= 7^2 : 4^2 = 49 : 16$

Use the fact that the triangles are similar to write two fractions involving x. You can equate these and rearrange to form a quadratic equation.

There are two solutions to the quadratic equation, but only one is a positive number.

 **Problem solved!**

There might be more than one way to tackle a problem. The method shown here uses the fact that if the ratio of lengths in similar shapes is $a : b$, the ratio of areas will be $a^2 : b^2$. You could also use $\frac{1}{2}ab \sin\theta$ to find the areas of both triangles.

1. The diagram shows two right-angled triangles.

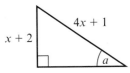

4x + 1

x + 2

a

x − 1

x + 1

b

sin a = sin b

Find the value of x. Give your answer correct to
3 significant figures.　　　　　**(5 marks)**

💡 **Knowledge check**

$$\sin x = \frac{\text{opposite}}{\text{hypotenuse}}$$

⚙ **Problem solved!**

The expressions on
the diagram represent
lengths, so they must
be positive numbers.
One length is
x − 1, so x > 1.

x = ...

2. B, C and D are points on the
circumference of a circle, and A is a
point outside the circle. AB and AD are
tangents to the circle.

Angle BCD = x − 12° and
angle BAD = x.

Find the value of x.　　　　**(5 marks)**

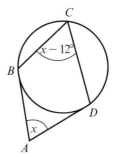

C

x − 12°

B

D

x

A

Draw the centre of
the circle O on the
diagram, then add in
the lines BO and OD.

⚠ **Examiner's hint**

Check that your
answers make sense.
The diagram isn't to
scale so you can't
measure, but the
answers should look
about right. In this
case, x is between
45° and 90°.

x = ...

Cumulative frequency graphs

What's it all about?

A cumulative frequency graph shows you how many data values were **less than** a particular amount.

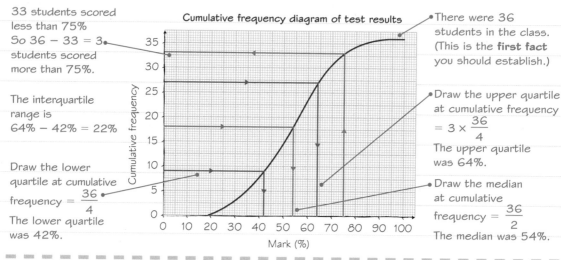

Cumulative frequency diagram of test results

33 students scored less than 75% So 36 − 33 = 3 students scored more than 75%.

There were 36 students in the class. (This is the **first fact** you should establish.)

The interquartile range is 64% − 42% = 22%

Draw the upper quartile at cumulative frequency $= 3 \times \dfrac{36}{4}$
The upper quartile was 64%.

Draw the lower quartile at cumulative frequency $= \dfrac{36}{4}$
The lower quartile was 42%.

Draw the median at cumulative frequency $= \dfrac{36}{2}$
The median was 54%.

Box plots

Box plots show the median, upper and lower quartiles, and the largest and smallest values of a set of data.

Half the weights were between 60 kg and 78 kg.
25% of the weights were greater than 78 kg.

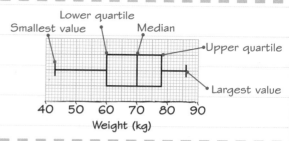

Smallest value | Lower quartile | Median | Upper quartile | Largest value

Weight (kg)

Worked example

The box plot gives information about the heights, in metres, of the trees in a park.

There are 162 trees in the park. Estimate the number of trees that are less than 10 m tall.

(1 mark)

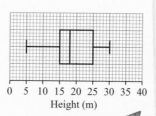

Height (m)

12.5% of 162 $= \dfrac{12.5}{100} \times 162 = 20.25$

20 is a good estimate.

10 m is not one of the measures of location given on the box plot. But it is **half way** between the smallest value (5 m) and the lower quartile (15 m). 25% of the data values lie in this range, so it is a good estimate that 12.5% of the trees are less than 10 m tall.

Exam practice

The reaction times of 120 students were recorded using a computer program.

Read each statement carefully before deciding whether it is true or false.

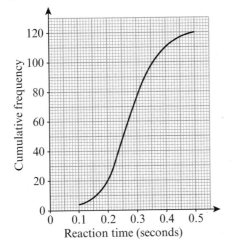

Cumulative frequency vs Reaction time (seconds)

💡**Knowledge check**

The lower quartile is $\frac{1}{4}$ of the way through the data, and the upper quartile is $\frac{3}{4}$ of the way through the data.

(a) Write **T** (true) or **F** (false) for each statement.　**(2 marks)**

A The quickest reaction time recorded was 0.1 seconds. ☐

B 20 students recorded a reaction time of 0.2 seconds. ☐

C More than half the students recorded a reaction time of 0.3 seconds or less. ☐

(b) Draw a box plot for this data.　**(3 marks)**

⚠**Examiner's hint**

Box plots should always be drawn on graph paper using a ruler and a sharp pencil. Remember to include a scale.

A student is chosen at random from the group.

(c) Find the probability that the student recorded a reaction time between 0.2 and 0.3 seconds.　**(3 marks)**

Work out the number of students who recorded a reaction time between 0.2 and 0.3 seconds and write this as a fraction of 120.

....

120

Histograms

What's it all about?

In a histogram the **area** of each bar is proportional to the frequency. The vertical axis is labelled 'frequency density', and you can find frequencies using the formula:

Frequency = Frequency density × Class width

Estimating frequencies

You can use the area under a histogram to estimate frequencies. An estimate for the **number** of maggots between 1mm and 2mm long is:

$0.5 \times 22 + 0.5 \times 6 = 14$

You might need to answer proportion questions about histograms in your exam. The total frequency is:

$1 \times 14 + 0.5 \times 22 + 1.5 \times 6 = 34$

So an estimate for the **proportion** of maggots between 1mm and 2mm long is: $\frac{14}{34} = 0.4117\ldots$ or 41% (2 s.f.)

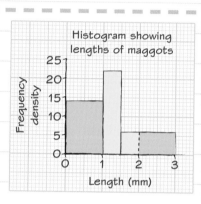

Histogram showing lengths of maggots

Worked example

The histogram shows the masses of onions in a crate.

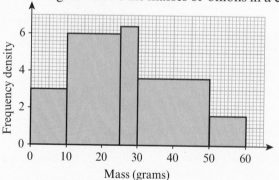

Estimate the lower quartile of the masses of the onions in the crate.
(4 marks)

Total area = $10 \times 3 + 15 \times 6 + 5 \times 6.4$
$\qquad + 20 \times 3.6 + 10 \times 1.6 = 240$

Area of first bar = 30

Area of second bar = 90

Lower quartile ≈ 15 grams

Work out the frequency for each bar by multiplying the class width by the frequency density.

Problem solved!

In a histogram, frequency is proportional to area. If you draw a vertical line at the lower quartile, $\frac{1}{4}$ of the total area of the histogram will lie to the left of this line.

The lower quartile lies approximately $\frac{1}{3}$ of the way through the second bar.

Exam practice

This histogram gives information about the diameters of trees in a park.

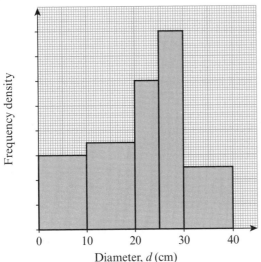

Diameter, d (cm)

Problem solved!

There is no scale on the vertical axis, so you need to work it out using the information given. The $0 < d \leqslant 10$ class has a frequency of 6, so the frequency density for this class is $\frac{6}{10} = 0.6$.

There were 6 trees in the park with a diameter between 0 cm and 10 cm.

(a) Complete the frequency table for this information.

For each class, multiply the frequency density by the class width to find the frequency.

Diameter (d cm)	Frequency
$0 < d \leqslant 10$	6
$10 < d \leqslant 20$	
$20 < d \leqslant 25$	
$25 < d \leqslant 30$	
$30 < d \leqslant 40$	

(3 marks)

(b) Find an estimate for the median diameter of the trees in the park. **(2 marks)**

Work out the total frequency (or the total area), then use proportion to estimate the point on the graph which divides the total area into two equal parts.

....

Representing probabilities

What's it all about?

A **tree diagram** can be used to show two or more events that happen one after the other. This tree diagram shows the probabilities when two beads are picked from a bag containing 7 red beads and 3 blue beads.

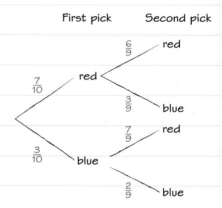

First pick   Second pick

$\frac{7}{10}$ red

$\frac{6}{9}$ red

$\frac{3}{9}$ blue

$\frac{3}{10}$ blue

$\frac{7}{9}$ red

$\frac{2}{9}$ blue

To find probabilities you multiply along the branches and add up the outcomes.

P(same colour) = P(red, red) + P(blue, blue)

$$= \frac{7}{10} \times \frac{6}{9} + \frac{3}{10} \times \frac{2}{9} = \frac{8}{15}$$

Worked example

This Venn diagram shows the burger toppings chosen by a group of 50 diners at a restaurant. The choices are avocado (*A*), broccoli (*B*) and cheese (*C*).

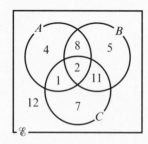

Two diners are picked at random.

Find the probability that both diners had a cheeseburger with broccoli and no avocado. **(2 marks)**

$$\frac{11}{50} \times \frac{10}{49} = \frac{11}{245}$$

Knowledge check

You can show frequencies on a Venn diagram. The section with the number 11 shows the number of diners who ordered broccoli **and** cheese, but **not** avocado.

The probability that the first diner had a cheeseburger with broccoli but no avocado is $\frac{11}{50}$. After that there were 10 diners left who ordered the same type of burger, and 49 diners left in total.

Exam practice

1. Each day Meg chooses between wearing a skirt and wearing trousers. The probability that she will choose a skirt is 0.6
If she chooses a skirt, the probability that she will wear trainers is 0.15
If she chooses trousers, the probability that she will wear trainers is 0.45

(a) Complete this probability tree diagram.

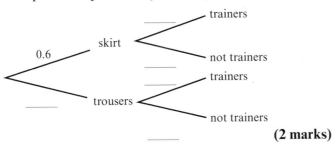

(2 marks)

(b) Find the probability Meg wears trainers to school.
(3 marks)

2. An Indian restaurant recorded the bread choices at 100 tables.
56 tables ordered naan, 22 tables ordered roti and 40 tables ordered paratha.
There were 8 tables that ordered naan and roti, 19 that ordered naan and paratha, and 15 that ordered roti and paratha.
6 tables ordered all three types of bread.

Two tables were picked at random. Work out the probability that they **both** ordered **only** paratha. **(5 marks)**

> 💡 **Knowledge check**
> The probability that an event **does not** happen is 1 minus the probability that it **does** happen.

> 💡 **Knowledge check**
> There are two outcomes to consider:
> - skirt and trainers
> - trousers and trainers

> ⚙️ **Problem solved!**
> Draw your own Venn diagram to solve this problem. Draw three intersecting circles, as in the Venn diagram opposite. Start by filling in 6 at the centre of your diagram, to represent the 6 tables that ordered all three types of bread.

> The total of all the frequencies in your Venn diagram should add up to 100.

123, 127

Probability and algebra

What's it all about?

You can solve some problems using probability facts and algebra. Watch out for selection **without replacement**. After the first pick, the total number of items has been reduced by 1, so the probabilities change for the second pick.

Add or multiply?

Events are **mutually exclusive** if they can't **both** happen at the same time. For mutually exclusive events:

$$P(A \text{ or } B) = P(A) + P(B)$$

Events are **independent** if the outcome of one doesn't affect the outcome of the other. For independent events:

$$P(A \text{ and } B) = P(A) \times P(B)$$

Worked example

A bag contains black and white counters. There are 7 fewer white counters than black counters.
Andrew takes two counters from the bag at random.
The probability that Andrew takes two black counters is $\frac{2}{5}$.

Work out the number of black counters originally in the bag. **(4 marks)**

x = number of black counters

So there are $x - 7$ white counters

P(first counter is black) $= \dfrac{x}{x + (x - 7)} = \dfrac{x}{2x - 7}$

P(both counters are black) $= \dfrac{x}{2x - 7} \times \dfrac{x - 1}{2x - 8}$

So $\dfrac{x}{2x - 7} \times \dfrac{x - 1}{2x - 8} = \dfrac{2}{5}$

$\qquad 5x(x - 1) = 2(2x - 7)(2x - 8)$

$\qquad 5x^2 - 5x = 8x^2 - 60x + 112$

$\quad 3x^2 - 55x + 112 = 0$

$\quad (3x - 7)(x - 16) = 0$

$x = \dfrac{7}{3}$ or $x = 16$

There were 16 black counters in the bag originally.

After the first pick the number of black counters has been reduced by 1, and the total number of counters has been reduced by 1. So the probability for the second pick is $\dfrac{x - 1}{2x - 8}$

Solve the quadratic equation by factorising or using the quadratic formula. x is the number of black counters so it must be a positive whole number.

Exam practice

1. A spinner can land on white or grey.

   The probability that it lands on grey is x, where x is less than $\frac{1}{2}$.

   Amy spins the spinner. She keeps spinning until it lands on grey.

   (a) Find an expression for the probability that she spins the spinner more than twice. You do not need to simplify your expression.   **(1 mark)**

   ....

   The probability that Amy spins the spinner **exactly** twice is $\frac{51}{400}$

   (b) Find the value of x.   **(4 marks)**

   $x = $ ....

Knowledge check

Consider the outcomes necessary to produce each result. In order for the spinner to be spun more than twice, the first two spins must be white.

Write an expression in terms of x for the probability that she spins the spinner exactly twice. Set this expression equal to $\frac{51}{400}$ and solve to find x.

2. A bag of sweets contains two flavours: strawberry and lemon. Nisha picks two sweets at random. The probability that the first sweet is lemon is $\frac{1}{5}$. The probability that both sweets are lemon is $\frac{9}{46}$

   Work out the **total** number of sweets that were in the bag initially. You must show all your working.   **(4 marks)**

Problem solved!

Write the number of lemon sweets as x and the number of strawberry sweets as y. You can use the two probabilities given in the question to write two simultaneous equations involving x and y.

Examiner's hint

Read the question carefully — you need to give the total number of sweets in the bag. This will be $x + y$

   ....

Answers

2–5. Knowledge check

1. C	2. B	3. C	4. A	5. C
6. A	7. A	8. D	9. B	10. C
11. C	12. D	13. B	14. A	15. B
16. A	17. C	18. B	19. D	20. A
21. D	22. C	23. B	24. A	25. D
26. C	27. C	28. A	29. B	30. D
31. C	32. B	33. D	34. C	35. D
36. C	37. B	38. A		

NUMBER

7. Indices and surds

1. (a) $\left(\frac{27}{64}\right)^{-\frac{2}{3}} = \left(\frac{64}{27}\right)^{\frac{2}{3}} = \frac{\left(\sqrt[3]{64}\right)^2}{\left(\sqrt[3]{27}\right)^2} = \frac{4^2}{3^2} = \frac{16}{9}$

   (b) $x = -1$, $y = \frac{5}{2}$, $z = -\frac{1}{2}$

   $x + y + z = 1$

2. $\frac{20 + \sqrt{12}}{\sqrt{3} + 1} = \frac{20 + \sqrt{12}}{\sqrt{3} + 1} \times \frac{\sqrt{3} - 1}{\sqrt{3} - 1}$

   $= \frac{20\sqrt{3} + \sqrt{12}\sqrt{3} - \sqrt{12} - 20}{3 - 1}$

   $= \frac{20\sqrt{3} - 2\sqrt{3} + 6 - 20}{2}$

   $= \frac{18\sqrt{3} - 14}{2}$

   $= 9\sqrt{3} - 7$

9. Accuracy and bounds

1. Lower bound for $a = 19.5\,\text{m}$

   Upper bound for $b = 17.5\,\text{m}$

   Lower bound for $c = \sqrt{19.5^2 - 17.5^2} = 8.60\,\text{m}$ (3 s.f.)

2.

	UB	LB
Distance	855 m	845 m
Speed	7.15 m/s	7.05 m/s

UB for time $= \frac{855}{7.05} = 121.276\ldots$

LB for time $= \frac{845}{7.15} = 118.181\ldots$

UB and LB both round to 120 seconds to 2 s.f.
(or nearest 10 s)

ALGEBRA

11. Brackets and factorising

1. $ac = 30 = 10 \times 3$ and $10 + 3 = 13$

   $5x^2 + 13x + 6 = 5x^2 + 10x + 3x + 6$

86

$= 5x(x + 2) + 3(x + 2)$

$= (5x + 3)(x + 2)$

2. $(2x + 1)(x - 5)(4x - 3)$

   $= (2x^2 - 9x - 5)(4x - 3)$

   $= 8x^3 - 36x^2 - 20x - 6x^2 + 27x + 15$

   $= 8x^3 - 42x^2 + 7x + 15$

   So $a = 8$, $b = -42$, $c = 7$ and $d = 15$

3. (a) $(x + y)(x - y)$

   (b) $(p^2 + q^2)^2 - (p^2 - q^2)^2$

   $= ((p^2 + q^2) + (p^2 - q^2))((p^2 + q^2) - (p^2 - q^2))$

   $= (2p^2)(2q^2)$

   $= 4p^2q^2$

13. Straight-line graphs

1. $y = 3x + c$ passes through $(2, 1)$

   $1 = 3(2) + c$

   So $c = -5$ and $y = 3x - 5$

2. Gradient $= \frac{-1 - 7}{8 - 2} = -\frac{4}{3}$

   $y = -\frac{4}{3}x + c$ passes through $(2, 7)$

   $7 = -\frac{4}{3}(2) + c$ so $c = \frac{29}{3}$

   $y = -\frac{4}{3}x + \frac{29}{3}$ so $4x + 3y = 29$

3. $\frac{k - 2}{1 - (-5)} = \frac{2k - k}{3 - 1}$

   $2k - 4 = 6k$

   $k = -1$

   Gradient $= \frac{-1 - 2}{1 - (-5)} = -\frac{1}{2}$

   $y = -\frac{1}{2}x + c$ passes through $(1, -1)$

   $-1 = -\frac{1}{2}(1) + c$ so $c = -\frac{1}{2}$

   $y = -\frac{1}{2}x - \frac{1}{2}$

15. Parallel and perpendicular

1. Gradient of AD = Gradient of $BC = \frac{0 - 4}{10 - 0} = -\frac{2}{5}$

   Perpendicular gradient $= \frac{5}{2}$

   $y = \frac{5}{2}x + c$ passes through $(10, 0)$

   $0 = \frac{5}{2}(10) + c$ so $c = -25$

   $y = \frac{5}{2}x - 25$

2. $5y - 2x = 3$

   $y = \frac{2}{5}x + \frac{3}{5}$

   So gradient $= \frac{2}{5}$

   $\frac{4 - 2p}{7 - p} = \frac{2}{5}$

$$4 - 2p = \frac{2}{5}(7 - p)$$
$$\frac{6}{5} = \frac{8}{5}p \text{ so } p = \frac{3}{4}$$

17. Quadratic equations

1. $(2x - 5)^2 = 5x$
$4x^2 - 20x + 25 = 5x$
$4x^2 - 25x + 25 = 0$
$(4x - 5)(x - 5) = 0$
$x = \frac{5}{4}$ or $x = 5$

2. $\frac{1}{2}(2x - 1)(x + 2) = 3 \times \frac{1}{2}(5)(x)$
$2x^2 + 3x - 2 = 15x$
$2x^2 - 12x - 2 = 0$
$x^2 - 6x - 1 = 0$
$$x = \frac{6 \pm \sqrt{(-6)^2 - 4 \times 1 \times (-1)}}{2}$$
$2x - 1$ is a length so $x > \frac{1}{2}$, so $x = 6.16$ (3 s.f.)

19. Sequences

1. (a)
$$\frac{2p}{8} = \frac{p + 12}{2p}$$
$$4p^2 = 8p + 96$$
$$p^2 - 2p - 24 = 0$$
$$(p + 4)(p - 6) = 0$$
p is positive so $p = 6$

(b) Common ratio is 1.5
8, 12, 18, 27, 40.5
5th term is 40.5

2. 3   10   21   36   55
  +7 +11 +15 +19
    +4   +4   +4
$2a = 4$ so $a = 2$
$u_n = 2n^2 + bn + c$

n	1	2	3	4	5
u_n	3	10	21	36	55
$2n^2$	2	8	18	32	50
$u_n - 2n^2$	1	2	3	4	5

$u_n - 2n^2 = n$
So $u_n = 2n^2 + n$

3. 3rd term $= k(19 + 3) = 22k$
4th term $= k(22k + 3) = 22k^2 + 3k$
$$22k^2 + 3k = 145$$
$$22k^2 + 3k - 145 = 0$$
$$(11k + 29)(2k - 5) = 0$$
k is positive so $k = \frac{5}{2}$
1st term $= 19 \div \frac{5}{2} - 3 = 4.6$

21. Completing the square

1. (a) $x^2 + 10x - 7 = (x + 5)^2 - 5^2 - 7$
$\qquad\qquad\qquad = (x + 5)^2 - 32$
(b) $x^2 + 10x - 7 = 0$
$(x + 5)^2 - 32 = 0$
$(x + 5)^2 = 32$
$x + 5 = \pm\sqrt{32}$
$x = -5 \pm \sqrt{32}$
$\quad = -5 \pm 4\sqrt{2}$

2. (a) $x^2 - 6x + 15 = (x - 3)^2 + 6$

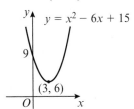

(b) No real solutions because graph does not intersect the x-axis.

23. Simultaneous equations

1. $x^2 + y^2 = 10$ ①
$y + 2x = 7$ ②
$y = 7 - 2x$ ③
Substitute ③ into ①:
$x^2 + (7 - 2x)^2 = 10$
$x^2 + 49 - 28x + 4x^2 = 10$
$5x^2 - 28x + 39 = 0$
$(5x - 13)(x - 3) = 0$
$x = 2.6$ or $x = 3$
$y = 7 - 2(2.6)$ $y = 7 - 2(3)$
$\quad = 1.8$ $= 1$
Points of intersection are (2.6, 1.8) and (3, 1)

2. $3x - 5 = x^2 - 3x + 4$
$0 = x^2 - 6x + 9$
$0 = (x - 3)^2$
There is only one solution, $x = 3$, and the line is not vertical, so there is only one point of intersection. Therefore the line must be a tangent to the curve.

25. Equation of a circle

1.

2. (a) $8^2 + 2^2 = k$
$\qquad k = 68$

87

(b) Gradient of $OP = \dfrac{2}{8} = \dfrac{1}{4}$

Gradient of tangent (perpendicular) $= -4$

$y = -4x + c$ passes through $(8, 2)$

$2 = -4(8) + c$

$c = 34$

Q is the y-intercept of the tangent so has coordinates $(0, 34)$.

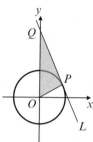

Area $OPQ = \dfrac{1}{2} \times 34 \times 8 = 136$ units²

27. Quadratic inequalities

1. $(x - 2)(3x + 4) \geqslant 2x^2$

$3x^2 - 2x - 8 \geqslant 2x^2$

$x^2 - 2x - 8 \geqslant 0$

$(x - 4)(x + 2) \geqslant 0$

$x \leqslant -2$ or $x \geqslant 4$

x is a length so cannot be negative so $x > 4$

2. $7 < \dfrac{x^2 + 7}{8}$

$56 < x^2 + 7$

$0 < x^2 - 49$

$0 < (x + 7)(x - 7)$

$x < -7$ or $x > 7$

$\dfrac{x^2 + 7}{8} < 11$

$x^2 + 7 < 88$

$x^2 - 81 < 0$

$(x + 9)(x - 9) < 0$

$-9 < x < 9$

Region that satisfies both inequalities: $-9 < x <$ -7 or $7 < x < 9$

29. Transforming graphs

1. (a) (b)

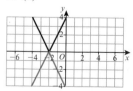 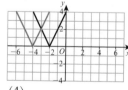

2. $y = f(x - 4)$: translation $\begin{pmatrix} 4 \\ 0 \end{pmatrix}$, so $(3, 1) \to (7, 1)$

$y = -f(x - 4)$: reflection in x-axis, so $(7, 1) \to (7, -1)$

$Q = (7, -1)$

31. Iteration

(a) $6(0) - (0)^3 - 3 = -3$

$6(1) - (1)^3 - 3 = 2$

There is a change of sign so the there is a solution between $x = 0$ and $x = 1$.

(b) $6x - x^3 = 3$

$x(6 - x^2) = 3$

$x = \dfrac{3}{6 - x^2}$

(c) $x_0 = 1$

$x_1 = \dfrac{3}{6 - x_0{}^2} = 0.6$

$x_2 = \dfrac{3}{6 - x_1{}^2} = 0.5319\ldots$

$x_3 = \dfrac{3}{6 - x_2{}^2} = 0.5247\ldots$

$x_4 = \dfrac{3}{6 - x_3{}^2} = 0.5240\ldots$

$x = 0.52$

(d) $6(0.515) - (0.515)^3 - 3 = -0.0465\ldots$

$6(0.525) - (0.525)^3 - 3 = 0.00529\ldots$

There is a change of sign so the answer is between 0.515 and 0.525 which is 0.52 is correct to 2 d.p.

33. Algebraic fractions

1. $\dfrac{9x^2 - 1}{3x^2 - 8x - 3} = \dfrac{(3x + 1)(3x - 1)}{(3x + 1)(x - 3)}$

$= \dfrac{3x - 1}{x - 3}$

2. (a) $\dfrac{6}{x} - \dfrac{2}{x + 2} = \dfrac{6(x + 2)}{x(x + 2)} - \dfrac{2x}{x(x + 2)}$

$= \dfrac{6x + 12 - 2x}{x(x + 2)}$

$= \dfrac{4x + 12}{x(x + 2)}$

(b) $\dfrac{6}{x} - \dfrac{2}{x + 2} + \dfrac{1}{2} = 0$

$\dfrac{4x + 12}{x(x + 2)} = -\dfrac{1}{2}$

$4x + 12 = -\dfrac{1}{2}x^2 - x$

$x^2 + 10x + 24 = 0$

$(x + 4)(x + 6) = 0$

$x = -4$ or $x = -6$

3. $\dfrac{3x}{x^2 - 5x} \div \dfrac{12x + 6}{2x^2 - 9x - 5} = \dfrac{3x}{x^2 - 5x} \times \dfrac{2x^2 - 9x - 5}{12x + 6}$

$= \dfrac{3x}{x(x - 5)} \times \dfrac{(2x + 1)(x - 5)}{6(2x + 1)}$

$= \dfrac{3(x - 5)}{6(x - 5)}$

$= \dfrac{3}{6} = \dfrac{1}{2}$

35. Functions

1. (a) $fg(x) = 1 - (3x - 1)^2$

$$= 1 - (9x^2 - 6x + 1)$$
$$= 6x - 9x^2$$
$$= 3x(2 - 3x)$$

(b) $0 = 3x - 1$

$x = \dfrac{1}{3}$ so $g^{-1}(0) = \dfrac{1}{3}$

2. $f(2) = 7$ so $2p + q = 7$ ①

$g^{-1}(35) = \dfrac{35 - 2}{3} = 11$

$f(3) = g^{-1}(35)$ so $3p + q = 11$ ②

② − ①: $p = 4$

Substitute into ①:

$8 + q = 7$ so $q = -1$

37. Algebraic proof

1. $n^2 - n = n(n - 1)$

If n is odd then $(n - 1)$ is even and vice versa, so
$n^2 - n = \text{ODD} \times \text{EVEN} = \text{EVEN}$

2. $(2n + 1)^2 + (2n + 3)^2 + (2n + 5)^2$
$= (4n^2 + 4n + 1) + (4n^2 + 12n + 9) + (4n^2 + 20n + 25)$
$= 12n^2 + 36n + 35$
$= 12(n^2 + 3n + 3) - 1$

n is an integer so $n^2 + 3n + 3$ is an integer. So the sum of any three consecutive odd numbers must be one less than a multiple of 12.

3. nth term $= 14 - 3n$

Consider pth and qth terms.

$(14 - 3p)^2 + (14 - 3q) = 9p^2 - 84p - 3q + 210$
$\qquad\qquad\qquad\qquad = 3(3p^2 - 28p - q + 70)$

$3p^2 - 28p - q + 70$ must be an integer, so the square of the pth term plus the qth term must be a multiple of 3.

39. Estimating gradients

(a) At 58 seconds the vacuum cleaner is travelling at approximately 1.7 m/s (but is not accelerating) *or* the graph is a velocity–time graph so gradient shows acceleration, not velocity.

(b)
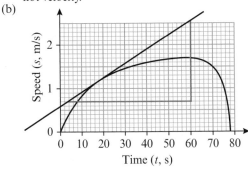

Gradient $\approx \dfrac{1.8}{56} = 0.032 \, \text{m/s}^2$ (± 0.005)

(c) The acceleration of the vacuum cleaner after 20 seconds.

(d) Because it is based on a measurement taken from a graph *or* because it depends on the accuracy of the tangent and triangle.

41. Areas under curves

(a)
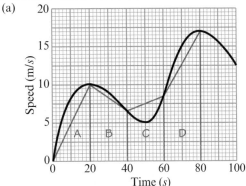

Area A $= \dfrac{1}{2} \times 20 \times 10 = 100$

Area B $= \dfrac{1}{2} \times 20 \times (10 + 6.5) = 165$

Area C $= \dfrac{1}{2} \times 20 \times (6.5 + 8.5) = 150$

Area D $= \dfrac{1}{2} \times 20 \times (8.5 + 17) = 255$

Total area $= 100 + 165 + 150 + 255 = 670 \, (\pm 20)$

(b) Not clear whether it is an underestimate or an overestimate

(c) Some of the trapeziums are above the curve and some are below.

43. Using algebra

1. (a) Length $= x + (x - 1) = 2x - 1$
$(2x - 1)(x + 3) = 99$
$2x^2 + 6x - x - 3 = 99$
$2x^2 + 5x = 102$

(b) $2x^2 + 5x - 102 = 0$
$(2x + 17)(x - 6) = 0$
x must be positive, so $x = 6$
Dimensions of rectangle are $9 \, \text{m} \times 11 \, \text{m}$
Perimeter $= 9 + 11 + 9 + 11 = 40 \, \text{m}$

2. $n = 0.1363636363\ldots$
$100n = 13.6363636\ldots$
$99n = 13.5$
$n = \dfrac{135}{990} = \dfrac{3}{22}$

RATIO & PROPORTION

45. Ratio and proportion

1. $2(x - 1) = 3(y - 1)$
$2x - 3y = -1$ ①
$x + 2 = 3(y - 4)$

$x - 3y = -14$ ②

① − ②:

$x = 13$

Substitute into ②:

$13 - 3y = -14$

$y = 9$

2. $4AB = 11BC$ so the perimeter of $ABCD$ is:

$$AB + \frac{4}{11}AB + \frac{4}{11}AB + AB = \frac{30}{11}AB$$

$4EF = 5FG$ so the perimeter of $EFGH$ is:

$$EF + \frac{4}{5}EF + \frac{4}{5}EF + EF = \frac{18}{5}EF$$

So $\frac{30}{11}AB = \frac{18}{5}EF$

$25AB = 33EF$

So the ratio $AB:EF$ is $33:25$

47. Growth and decay

1. (a) £2000 × 1.013^5 = £2133.42 (2 d.p.)

(b) 5000 × m^6 = 5615, where m is the multiplier
for a $p\%$ increase

$$m^6 = 1.123$$

$$m = \sqrt[6]{1.123} = 1.019\,522\ldots$$

$$p = 1.95 \text{ (3 s.f.)}$$

2. (a) $j = 87$, $k = 0.92$

(b) $x_0 = 87$

$x_1 = 87 \times 0.92 = 80.04$

$x_2 = 80.04 \times 0.92 = 73.6368$

$x_3 = 73.6368 \times 0.92 = 67.7$ (3 s.f.)

(c) In real life the temperature of the tea will
not fall below room temperature / will be
close to zero.

49. Proportionality formulae

1. (a) Compare values for $q = 8$ and $q = 10$

$$10 \div 8 = 1.25$$

$$25 \div 12.8 = 1.953\,125 = 1.25^3$$

So $n = 3$

or find formula $p = 0.025q^3$

(b) $p = kq^3$

$$25 = k \times 10^3$$

$k = 0.025$ so $p = 0.025q^3$

(c) $p = 0.025 \times 12^3 = 43.2$

2. $y = kb^2$

$15 = k \times 5^2$ so $k = \frac{3}{5}$

So $y = \frac{3}{5}b^2$ ①

$b = \frac{k}{x}$

$8 = \frac{k}{10}$ so $k = 80$

So $b = \frac{80}{x}$ ②

Substitute ② into ①:

$$y = \frac{3}{5}\left(\frac{80}{x}\right)^2$$

$$= \frac{3 \times 6400}{5x^2}$$

$$= \frac{3840}{x^2}$$

GEOMETRY & MEASURES

51. Trigonometry

1. Exterior angle of S $= \frac{360°}{12} = 30°$

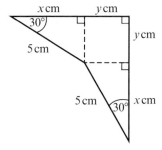

$x = 5\cos 30° = 4.330\ldots$ cm

$y = 5\sin 30° = 2.5$ cm

Area of triangle $= \frac{1}{2} \times 2.5 \times 4.330\ldots = 5.412\ldots$ cm^2

Area of square $= 2.5^2 = 6.25$ cm^2

Total area of D $= 6.25 + 2 \times 5.412\ldots$

$= 17.1$ cm^2 (3 s.f.)

2.

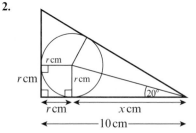

$\tan 20° = \dfrac{r}{x}$

$x = \dfrac{r}{\tan 20°} = 2.747r$

So $r + 2.747r = 10$

$3.747r = 10$ so $r = 2.67$ (3 s.f.)

53. Sine and cosine rules

1. (a) $PR^2 = 14^2 + 8^2 - 2 \times 14 \times 8 \times \cos 56°$

$$= 134.74\ldots$$

$PR = 11.6$ (3 s.f.)

(b) $\dfrac{\sin \angle QRP}{7} = \dfrac{\sin 80°}{11.607\ldots}$

$\sin \angle QRP = 0.5938\ldots$

$\angle QRP = 36.4°$ (3 s.f.)

2. $\angle BDA = 180° - 37° - 64° = 79°$

$$\frac{BD}{\sin 37°} = \frac{16}{\sin 64°}$$

$$BD = 10.713\ldots$$

So $\cos \angle BDC = \dfrac{18^2 + 10.713\ldots^2 - 25^2}{2 \times 18 \times 10.713\ldots}$

$$= -0.4828\ldots$$

$$\angle BDC = 118.871\ldots°$$

So $x = 360° - 79° - 118.871\ldots° = 162.1°$ (1 d.p.)

55. Sectors of circles

1. $AB = \dfrac{52}{360} \times 2\pi r = 0.907\,57\,r$

So $2r + 0.907\,57\,r = 10$

$$2.907\,57\,r = 10$$

$$r = 3.44\,\text{cm} \ (3 \text{ s.f.})$$

2. Area of sector $ABC = \dfrac{35}{360} \times \pi \times 12^2 = 14\pi\,\text{cm}^2$

Vertical height of $\triangle ABM = 12 \sin 35° = 6.8829\ldots$

Area of $\triangle ABM = \dfrac{1}{2} \times 6 \times 6.8829\ldots = 20.6487\ldots$

Shaded area $= 14\pi - 20.6487\ldots = 23.3\,\text{cm}^2 \ (3 \text{ s.f.})$

57. Triangles and segments

1. In $\triangle ABC$, $\angle ACB = 70°$ (alternate angles)

$AC = 2.3\,\text{m}$ (AC and AD are radii of the same circle)

$$\frac{\sin \angle ABC}{2.3} = \frac{\sin 70°}{2.8}$$

$$\sin \angle ABC = 0.7718\ldots$$

$$\angle ABC = 50.523\ldots°$$

$\angle BAC = 180° - 70° - 50.523\ldots° = 59.476\ldots°$

So area $ABC = \dfrac{1}{2} \times 2.3 \times 2.8 \times \sin 59.476\ldots°$

$$= 2.7737\ldots$$

Area of sector $ACD = \dfrac{70}{360} \times \pi \times 2.3^2$

$$= 3.2314\ldots\,\text{m}^2$$

Area of shaded shape $= 2.7737\ldots + 3.2314\ldots$

$$= 6.01\,\text{m}^2 \ (3 \text{ s.f.})$$

2. $\triangle ABC$ is equilateral, so area $= \dfrac{1}{2} r^2 \sin 60° = \dfrac{\sqrt{3}}{4} r^2$

Area of one sector $= \dfrac{60}{360} \pi r^2 = \dfrac{1}{6} \pi r^2$

Area of shape = 3 sectors − 2 triangles

$$= 3 \times \frac{1}{6} \pi r^2 - 2 \times \frac{\sqrt{3}}{4} r^2$$

$$= \frac{1}{2} \pi r^2 - \frac{\sqrt{3}}{2} r^2$$

$$= \frac{1}{2} r^2 (\pi - \sqrt{3})$$

59. 3D lengths and angles

1. $14^2 + 22^2 + CH^2 = 27^2$

$$CH^2 = 49$$

$$CH = 7\,\text{m}$$

Volume of cuboid $= 14 \times 22 \times 7 = 2156\,\text{m}^3$

2. $AC = \sqrt{10^2 + 10^2} = \sqrt{200}$

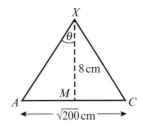

In $\triangle AMX$: $\quad \tan\theta = \dfrac{\frac{1}{2}\sqrt{200}}{8}$

$$= 0.8838\ldots$$

$$\theta = 41.4729\ldots°$$

So $\angle AXC = 2\theta = 82.9°$ (3 s.f.)

61. Transformations

1.

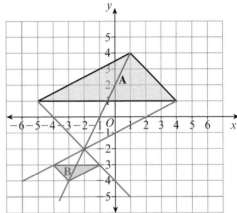

2.

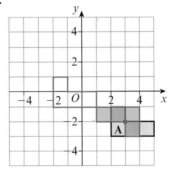

Invariant point is $(3, -2)$

63. Congruent triangles

1. $AB = EF$ (opposite sides of parallelogram)

$BC = ED$ (opposite sides of square)

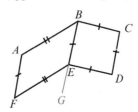

∠ABE = ∠FEG (corresponding angles in parallel lines)

∠EBC = ∠GED (right angles)

So ∠ABC = ∠FED

So ΔABC is congruent to ΔFED (SAS)

So AC = FD (corresponding sides in congruent triangles)

2. (a) ∠EAD = ∠CBE (given)

   ∠AED = ∠BEC (common angle)

   AE = EB (equal sides of isosceles triangle)

   So ΔADE is congruent to ΔBCE (AAS)

   (b) CE = DE (corresponding sides in congruent triangles)

   And AE = EB (equal sides of isosceles triangle)

   BD = BE − DE and AC = AE − EC

   so BD = AC

65. Similar shapes 1

1. (a) $AB : BC = 3 : 2$ so $AB = \frac{3}{5}AC$

   Similarly $AD = \frac{3}{5}AE$

   ∠BAD = ∠CAE (common angle)

   Two sides are in the same ratio and the included angle is equal, so ΔABD and ΔACE are similar.

   (b) $3 : 2 = 10.5 : 7$ so $AB = 10.5$ cm and $AC = 17.5$ cm

   $\frac{CE}{BD} = \frac{AC}{AB}$

   $\frac{CE}{6} = \frac{17.5}{10.5}$ so $CE = 10$ cm

2. If AF and BG are corresponding sides:

   $\frac{x+5}{5} = \frac{10}{4}$

   $x + 5 = 12.5$

   $x = 7.5$

   If AF and GD are corresponding sides:

   $\frac{x+5}{4} = \frac{10}{5}$

   $x + 5 = 8$ so $x = 3$

67. Similar shapes 2

1. $k^2 = \frac{2000}{6480}$ so $k = \frac{5}{9}$

   So volume $\mathbf{B} = 1458 \times \left(\frac{5}{9}\right)^3 = 250$ cm³

2. volume $\mathbf{A}$: volume $\mathbf{B} = 27 : 64$

   So height $\mathbf{A}$: height $\mathbf{B} = 3 : 4$

   $3 : 4 = 9 : 12$ and $6 : 7 = 12 : 14$, so height $\mathbf{A}$: height $\mathbf{B}$: height $\mathbf{C} = 9 : 12 : 14$

   So height $\mathbf{A}$: height $\mathbf{C} = 9 : 14$

   So surface area $\mathbf{A}$: surface area $\mathbf{C} = 81 : 196$

69. Volume and surface area

1. $\frac{x + 2.4}{x} = \frac{4.5}{3}$

   $3(x + 2.4) = 4.5x$

   $1.5x = 7.2$

   $x = 4.8$

   Height of large cone = 4.8 + 2.4 = 7.2 cm

   Height of small cone = 4.8 cm

   Volume of frustum

   $= \frac{1}{3}\pi(2.25)^2 \times 7.2 - \frac{1}{3}\pi(1.5)^2 \times 4.8$

   $= \frac{171}{20}\pi$ cm³ or 26.9 cm³ (3 s.f.)

2. Area of cross-section above water (segment)

   $= \frac{115}{360}\pi \times 20^2 - \frac{1}{2} \times 20^2 \times \sin 115°$

   $= 220.164\ldots$ cm²

   Area of submerged cross-section

   $= \pi \times 20^2 - 220.164\ldots = 1036.47\ldots$

   Volume of submerged section = 120 × 1036.47…

   = 124 000 cm³ or 0.124 m³ (3 s.f.)

71. Using circle theorems

1. ∠ADB = 52° (alternate segment theorem)

   ∠BAD = 180° − 52° − 61° = 67° (angles in a triangle add up to 180°)

   ∠BCD = 180° − 67° = 113° (opposite angles in a cyclic quadrilateral add up to 180°)

2. (a) ∠PBC = ∠PDA (angles in the same segment)

   ∠APD = ∠CPB (common angle)

   ∠DAB = ∠DCB (angles in the same segment)

   ∠PCB = 180° − ∠DCB and

   ∠PAD = 180° − ∠DAB

   (angles on a straight line add up to 180°)

   So ∠PCB = ∠PAD

   So ΔPBC and ΔPDA are similar (AAA)

   (b) $\frac{PA}{PC} = \frac{PD}{PB}$ so $PA \times PB = PC \times PD$

73. Proving circle theorems

1. (a) ∠ADB = 90° (angle in a semicircle is 90°)

   ∠BAC = 90° (angle between a tangent and a radius is 90°)

   So ∠BAD = 90° − y

   So x + 90° − y + 90° = 180° (angles in ΔABD add up to 180°)

   So x − y = 0 and x = y

   (b) Neil is not correct as the argument only works if AB is a diameter, whereas the alternate segment theorem applies to any chord AB.

2. Let $\angle ABO = x$ and $\angle CBO = y$

$\triangle AOB$ and $\triangle BOC$ are isosceles so $\angle BOA = 180° - 2x$ and $\angle BOC = 180° - 2y$ (base angles of an isosceles triangle are equal and angles in a triangle add up to 180°)

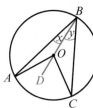

So $\angle DOA = 2x$ and $\angle DOC = 2y$ (angles on a straight line add up to 180°)

So $\angle AOC = 2x + 2y = 2(x + y) = 2 \times \angle ABC$ as required.

75. Vectors

1. $\overrightarrow{AB} = \overrightarrow{AM} + \overrightarrow{MB}$

$= -\mathbf{a} + \dfrac{1}{5}\overrightarrow{MC} = -\mathbf{a} + \dfrac{1}{5}(-\mathbf{a} + 3\mathbf{b}) = -\dfrac{6}{5}\mathbf{a} + \dfrac{3}{5}\mathbf{b}$

$\overrightarrow{AN} = \overrightarrow{AO} + \overrightarrow{ON} = -2\mathbf{a} + \mathbf{b}$

So $-\dfrac{6}{5}\mathbf{a} + \dfrac{3}{5}\mathbf{b} = k(-2\mathbf{a} + \mathbf{b})$

$k = \dfrac{3}{5}$

2. Let $\overrightarrow{AB} = \mathbf{a}$ and $\overrightarrow{AD} = \mathbf{b}$

So $\overrightarrow{AP} = \dfrac{4}{5}\mathbf{a}$, $\overrightarrow{DQ} = \dfrac{2}{5}\mathbf{a}$ and $\overrightarrow{AM} = \dfrac{1}{2}\mathbf{b}$

$\overrightarrow{PQ} = \overrightarrow{PA} + \overrightarrow{AD} + \overrightarrow{DQ}$

$= -\dfrac{4}{5}\mathbf{a} + \mathbf{b} + \dfrac{2}{5}\mathbf{a} = \mathbf{b} - \dfrac{2}{5}\mathbf{a}$

$\overrightarrow{PN} = \overrightarrow{PA} + \overrightarrow{AM} + \overrightarrow{MN}$

$= -\dfrac{4}{5}\mathbf{a} + \dfrac{1}{2}\mathbf{b} + \dfrac{1}{2}\left(\dfrac{1}{2}\mathbf{b} + \mathbf{a}\right)$

$= \dfrac{3}{4}\mathbf{b} - \dfrac{3}{10}\mathbf{a} = \dfrac{3}{4}\left(\mathbf{b} - \dfrac{2}{5}\mathbf{a}\right)$

So $\overrightarrow{PN} = \dfrac{3}{4}\overrightarrow{PQ}$ so P, N and Q lie on the same straight line.

77. Geometry and algebra

1. $\sin\theta = \dfrac{\text{opp}}{\text{hyp}}$

$\dfrac{x + 2}{4x + 1} = \dfrac{x - 1}{x + 1}$

$(x + 2)(x + 1) = (x - 1)(4x + 1)$

$x^2 + 3x + 2 = 4x^2 - 3x - 1$

$3x^2 - 6x - 3 = 0$

$x^2 - 2x - 1 = 0$

$x = 1 \pm \sqrt{2}$

$x - 1$ is a length so $x > 1$, so $x = 2.41$ (3 s.f.)

2. $\angle BOD = 2(x - 12°)$ (angle subtended at centre is twice angle subtended at circumference)

$\angle BOD = 360° - x - 90° - 90°$
$= 180° - x$ (angles in a quadrilateral add up to 360° and angle between a tangent and a radius = 90°)

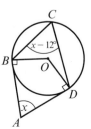

So $2x - 24 = 180 - x$

$3x = 204$

$x = 68°$

STATISTICS & PROBABILITY

79. Cumulative frequency graphs

(a) **A** True

B False (20 students recorded a reaction time $\leqslant 0.2$ s)

C True (approx. 76 out of 120 students recorded a reaction time $\leqslant 0.3$ s)

(b)

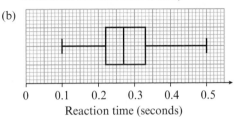

(c) $76 - 20 = 56$ students recorded a reaction time between 0.2 and 0.3 seconds

$\dfrac{56}{120}$ or $\dfrac{7}{15}$

81. Histograms

(a) For $0 < d \leqslant 10$ class:

frequency density $= \dfrac{6}{10} = 0.6$

Diameter, d (cm)	Frequency
$0 < d \leqslant 10$	6
$10 < d \leqslant 20$	$0.7 \times 10 = 7$
$20 < d \leqslant 25$	$1.2 \times 5 = 6$
$25 < d \leqslant 30$	$1.6 \times 5 = 8$
$30 < d \leqslant 40$	$0.5 \times 10 = 5$

(b) Total frequency $= 6 + 7 + 6 + 8 + 5 = 32$
13 trees $\leqslant 20$ cm and 19 trees $\leqslant 25$ cm so median is half-way between 20 and 25.
Median ≈ 22.5 cm

83. Representing probabilities

1. (a)

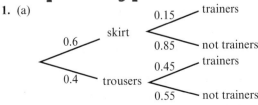

(b) $P(\text{trainers}) = 0.6 \times 0.15 + 0.4 \times 0.45 = 0.27$

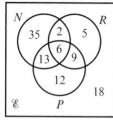

$$P(\text{only paratha}) = \frac{12}{100}$$

$$P(\text{both only paratha}) = \frac{12}{100} \times \frac{11}{99} = \frac{1}{75}$$

85. Probability and algebra

1. (a) Requires first two spins to be white−white, so
   P(at least twice) = $(1 - x)^2$

   (b) Requires white−grey, so
   P(exactly twice) = $(1 - x)x$

   $$x(1 - x) = \frac{51}{400}$$

$$400x^2 - 400x + 51 = 0$$
$$(20x - 3)(20x - 17) = 0$$
$$x < \frac{1}{2} \text{ so } x = \frac{3}{20} \text{ or } 0.15$$

2. x = number of lemon sweets and
   y = number of strawberry sweets

   $$\frac{x}{x + y} = \frac{1}{5}$$
   $$5x = x + y$$
   $$4x - y = 0 \; ①$$
   $$\frac{x - 1}{x + y - 1} = \frac{9}{46}$$
   $$46(x - 1) = 9(x + y - 1)$$
   $$46x - 46 = 9x + 9y - 9$$
   $$37x - 9y = 37 \; ②$$
   $$② - 9 \times ① : x = 37$$

   Substitute into ①: $4 \times 37 - y = 0$ so $y = 148$

   Total number of sweets initially in
   bag = 37 + 148 = 185

Published by Pearson Education Limited, 80 Strand, London, WC2R 0RL.

www.pearsonschoolsandfecolleges.co.uk

Copies of official specifications for all Pearson qualifications may be found on the website: qualifications.pearson.com

Text © Harry Smith and Pearson Education Limited 2019
Original illustrations © Pearson Education Limited 2019
Typeset and illustrated by
Newgen KnowledgeWorks Pvt. Ltd., Chennai, India
Produced by Newgen Publishing UK
Cover illustration by Miriam Sturdee

The right of Harry Smith to be identified as author of this work has been asserted by him in accordance with the Copyright, Designs and Patents Act 1988.

First published 2019

22 21 20 19
10 9 8 7 6 5 4 3 2 1

British Library Cataloguing in Publication Data
A catalogue record for this book is available from the British Library

ISBN 978 1 292 29428 5

Printed in Slovakia by Neografia

Acknowledgements
P 67: Figure of two mathematically similar sculptures based on the sculpture, Locking Piece by Henry Moore in Riverside Walk Gardens, London, UK from the photograph by Ashley Cooper Pics, Alamy Stock Photo
Alamy Stock Photo: Ashley Cooper Pics 67.

Notes from the publisher
1. While the publishers have made every attempt to ensure that advice on the qualification and its assessment is accurate, the official specification and associated assessment guidance materials are the only authoritative source of information and should always be referred to for definitive guidance.

   Pearson examiners have not contributed to any sections in this resource relevant to examination papers for which they have responsibility.

2. Pearson has robust editorial processes, including answer and fact checks, to ensure the accuracy of the content in this publication, and every effort is made to ensure this publication is free of errors. We are, however, only human, and occasionally errors do occur. Pearson is not liable for any misunderstandings that arise as a result of errors in this publication, but it is our priority to ensure that the content is accurate. If you spot an error, please do contact us at resourcescorrections@pearson.com so we can make sure it is corrected.